FARTHEST NORTH OBTAINED BY OFFICERS OF U. S. ARMY SIGNAL CORPS ARCTIC
EXPEDITION, 1881–1884. FIRST LIEUTENANT A. W. GREELY, ACTING
SIGNAL OFFICER, U. S. A., IN COMMAND.

From an original painting by Albert Operti, now in possession of the United
States Government.

THE POLAR REGIONS
IN THE
TWENTIETH CENTURY

THEIR
DISCOVERY AND INDUSTRIAL
EVOLUTION

BY

A. W. GREELY

MAJOR GENERAL U. S. ARMY, RETIRED

WITH ILLUSTRATIONS
AND MAPS

LITTLE, BROWN, AND COMPANY
BOSTON
1928

PREFACE

AMONG the striking industrial changes of the twentieth century is the increased utilization of the material resources of the polar regions. In earlier ages the polar oceans were chosen fields of stirring human activity, but now their products are subordinate to those of the lands. The antarctic seas hold their own in whaling, while the seas of Greenland and Barents are still productive.

Notable as have been the economic changes in Arctic Alaska and Northern Canada, they are less striking than the astonishing developments of Arctic Sweden and of Svalbard (Spitsbergen) Archipelago.

In connection with the accounts of these economic changes, there are presented such discoveries and explorations as have enabled man to transform these waste regions into industrial fields of vast material benefit.

This volume presents in summary more than eighty thousand pages of original narratives, in such form as will subserve the enquiries of busy men, who, on this subject of general interest, wish to know what, when and where, rather than how.

It is believed that no discovery of importance — geographic, scientific or of utilization — has been neglected. However, the wide and intricate phases of scientific research, briefly alluded to, are treated in the volumes quoted herein.

Topical treatment is followed, in preference to the usual chronological. Thus are presented sharper pictures of local conditions, and clearer ideas of sectional peculiarities, for the polar regions present as great variety as do the continents. The indulgence of the reader is craved for undue dwelling on the expedition in which the author was engaged.

Acknowledgment is made of the cordial spirit of international good will which has caused the governments of Canada, Iceland, Norway, Russia and Sweden to furnish information of value. The Bureaus of the United States and the National Geographic Society have likewise contributed.

A. W. GREELY

Washington, D. C.,
MARCH 27, 1928

CONTENTS

Contents

ILLUSTRATIONS

[ix]

THE POLAR REGIONS
IN THE TWENTIETH CENTURY

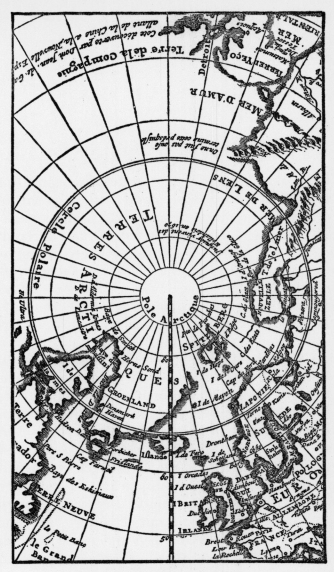

DELISLE'S TERRES ARCTIQUES, 1715

CHAPTER I

ARCTIC DISCOVERIES PRIOR TO 1800

THE most remarkable Arctic discoveries of recorded history are those made by the Norsemen, in or before the ninth century, which are summarized in the chapters on Greenland and Iceland. The extent of knowledge as to arctic geography at the commencement of the eighteenth century is shown by the map (page 1) of G. Delisle: "Voyages au Nord" (Amsterdam, 1715). Hudson Bay, Iceland, Jan Mayen and the archipelago of Spitsbergen are known and charted. While the southern half of Greenland was mapped, yet it was thought to be bisected by Frobisher Strait. Barely two centuries ago, more than one half of the arctic coasts were unknown to geographers. Novaya Zemlya was yet believed to be a part of the mainland of Asia. The great Siberian rivers, the Lena and Yenisei, are charted, as the delta of the Lena had been reached by Elisha Busa in one of his three voyages (1636–1639) to explore the Lena, Olenek and Yana. Deshnef's strait (Bering) and the Amur River valley are mapped under Yecco Land, an isolated province of Asia. Thence eastward to Baffin Bay is an uncharted area.

[3]

England had sent out repeated expeditions to navigate the Northeast Passage, among which were Chancellor and Willoughby, 1553–1554; Burroughs, 1556–1557; Pet and Jackman, 1680–1681. The final outcome of all these efforts had been the attainment of the Kara Sea, into which they could not penetrate. The three competitive voyages of the Dutch (1594–1597), under Barents, Nay and Tetgales, were primarily failures, though they visited the northern half of Novaya Zemlya. The explorations of Bering are recorded in Chapter II, and those of other Russian expeditions in Chapter XVII.

The earliest ventures in search of a northwest passage to China, while failures as to their primary object, were fruitful in geographic knowledge. The voyages of the Cabots (1497 and 1498) covered nearly eighteen hundred miles of the eastern coasts of America, in which they doubtless passed the mouth of Hudson Strait, their northern latitude being about 62° 30'. The cruises of Cortreal, Gomez and Verrazzano, between 1500 and 1524, failed in the quest, but opened a new field of oceanic industry. Their reports gave rise to the lucrative fisheries pursued by the Basques, Portuguese and Spaniards in the coast waters of Newfoundland between 1540 and 1570. The familiarity of these daring fishermen with the coasts of North America, and the range of their northern researches, were shown by the appearance of a new

[4]

strait (Hudson) on their sailing chart of 1558, and by the quite definite outlines of Hudson Bay in the atlas of Ortelius in 1570.

Doubtless it was the commercial successes of their southern competitors that caused England to renew the abandoned Northwest Quest, by a series of remarkable ventures, the most notable being those of Frobisher, Davis, Baffin and Hudson. Full accounts of these voyages have been published by the Hakluyt Society, as follows: Collinson, "Three Voyages of Martin Frobisher"; A. H. Markham, "Voyages of John Davis"; C. R. Markham, "Voyages of William Baffin"; and Asher, "Henry Hudson, Navigator."

Of Frobisher's efforts, Asher says: "He first gave national character to the search by bringing all the most eminent interests in the country — political and aristocratic, scientific and commercial — to bear on the enterprise." In his three voyages, 1576, 1577 and 1578, Frobisher determined the existence of a broad strait (Frobisher) in North America, navigable for hundreds of miles between latitudes 62° and 63° N. Also he rediscovered a second strait (Hudson), which he reported to be broad and easily navigable. Beyond this he contributed a mass of misleading geographic information, and brought to England a quantity of worthless earth, which he thought to be gold-bearing, that led to other disappointing voyages. Geographically his errors were grievous. He located

[5]

the south cape of Greenland in latitude 65° N.,
charted a mythical island (Busse); bisected
southern Greenland by Frobisher Strait; and
considered the mainland of America, which he
reached, as part of Greenland. These errors were
a continuing feature of arctic charts for many
years, perplexing explorers and geographers.
Moreover, they were the basis of vague theories
which found supporters in this generation, three
centuries later. His two navigable straits, however, encouraged belief in the existence of a waterway through America to the Pacific Ocean.

The first great advance in the discovery of the
promised Northwest Passage resulted from the
three voyages (1585, 1586 and 1588) of John Davis,
of Sandridge, an accomplished seaman, whose
abilities as a sailor were no less conspicuous than
his skill as a pilot and knowledge as a navigator.
In his first voyage he skirted the west coast of
Greenland to the neighborhood of Godthaab.
Turning west, he crossed the strait which now
bears his name, discovered Cape Dyer and, entering Cumberland Sound, nearly reached its head.
In 1586 he followed the American coast from Davis
Strait to southern Labrador, without noting the
entrance to Hudson Bay. In his final voyage he
turned to Greenland waters, where he sailed northward to the vicinity of Sanderson's Hope. On
June 30, 1587, he reached the astonishing latitude
of 72° 12′ N., then the highest northing in the

western hemisphere. Daring and skillful as have been many navigators of arctic waters in succeeding centuries, none have equaled — equipment con- sidered — the extraordinary voyages of Davis and Baffin, which were made in crafts whose tonnages were respectively sixty and fifty-five tons.

The voyages of Weymouth (1602) and of Knight and Hall (1605–1607) contributed practically noth- ing in the way of discoveries, and England gave way to Holland and Hudson.

The next honors were won by a man whose recorded life of action ran only four years, from 1607 to 1611. Four years is a brief period, but it was long enough for Henry Hudson to make a lasting impress on his own generation — one of great and experienced seamen — and to render his name imperishable in history. He visited almost all of the known arctic lands of Europe and America, and in whatever direction he employed his energies, unusual successes followed.

His first three voyages were under the auspices of Holland. The first, in 1607, is noted in Chap- ter XIX. It is a curious fact that his third voyage, in search of the Northeast Passage for Holland, was most famous for its outcome. Leaving Texel April 6, 1609, and finding progress east of Novaya Zemlya impossible, Hudson turned westward, and skirting the American coast southward, entered Hudson River on September 12, and remained there until October 4, then coasted down to Delaware Bay. Describing the Hudson "as fine a river as can be found", he ascended it about fifty leagues and had friendly relations with the Indians. Though this river had been discovered by Verrazzano in 1524, it was previously unnamed.

Hudson's final voyage, 1610, was under the auspices of England, and he was forced to quit the service of Holland. He sailed from London on April 17, in the *Discovery* to try "if through any of those inlets which Davis saw on the western side of Fretum Davis any passage might be found to the other ocean." Touching at Iceland, and later making the east coast of Greenland in 65° 30′ N. Hudson found the shore icebound. Standing southward, he was delayed by efforts to pass west through one of the many inlets, which were erroneously thought to be the fictitious strait of Frobisher. Finally he rounded capes Desolation and Farewell and sailing west entered a strait (Hudson), until he reached a point where he "found the sea more growne than any wee had since wee left England." He was in Hudson Bay. As already shown, Cabot, Davis and Weymouth had visited the mouth of Hudson Strait, and Portuguese fishermen had even entered the bay. However, the achievements of Hudson were so unusual, and his fate so tragic, as to justify cartographers in permanently attaching his name to the great inland sea, where, as elsewhere, he surpassed his predecessors in successful exploration.

[8]

His ship was beset by ice, his officers became mutinous, and his crew were struck with fear, yet Hudson continued his voyage. Following the shore of the bay, he reached its southeastern extremity, where he was frozen in on November 12, at James Bay. Breaking out in the spring of 1611, he attempted the exploration of the west coast, but his crew mutinied. On June 21, Hudson was forced into a shallop, with eight followers, and thus perished under unknown conditions.

Henry Hudson died living up to his heroic rule that men should "achieve what they had undertaken, or else give reason wherefore it will not be." If he failed to find the Northwest Passage, his discoveries in pursuance thereof eventuated in ensuring to England the enormous wealth of the game resources of Hudson Bay Territory. It was a fortunate supplement to his contribution — through his earlier voyages — of the whale fisheries of the Greenland Sea for the exploitation of Dutch and English whalers.

Sir Thomas Button entered Hudson Bay in 1614, and after wintering there crossed the bay from east to west, first navigator to do so. He explored the west shores from Nelson River northward to Southampton Island, discoveries which were confirmed by the voyage of Bylot in 1615. Unfortunately for his successors, Button believed that a passage to the South Sea could be found via the northwest part of Hudson Bay. It was

a century before this conjecture was completely
dispelled, by Parry.

The voyage of Jens Munk, who wintered in
Churchill River, was marked by disease and disaster; his discoveries on the west shore were
viewed with distrust. James, with the so-called
"Northwest" Fox, sailed in 1631, and was so
confident of making the passage that he carried
a letter from the King of England to the Emperor
of Japan. This explorer is best known by a quaint
and somewhat humorous account of the voyage,
styled "Northwest Fox." A few unimportant
islands were his only discoveries.

To close with efforts through Hudson Bay, it is
to be noted that the voyage of Middleton, 1741,
discovered Wager River and Repulse Bay, thus
affording convincing proof of the impossibility of
navigation from the Hudson Bay to the west.
Sir Arthur Dobbs questioned the accuracy of
Middleton's discoveries, claiming that Wager River
was a strait leading to the South Sea. To his
discomfiture, the captains — Moore and Smith — of
the *Dobbs* and *California*, sent out in 1746, reported
that the Wager was a river, not a strait.

The final attempt of the seventeenth century
was made over the only route by which a northwest
passage could be discovered, via Davis Strait.
The attempt was made by an able seaman and
dauntless explorer, William Baffin. In the *Discovery*, a tiny craft of fifty-five tons, he sailed from

Gravesend March 16, 1616, and sighted Greenland
May 14. Following the west coast, he passed
Sanderson's Hope, the farthest point of land of
Davis, but was stopped by the heavy ice on June
9, at Baffin Islands, 73° 54' N. latitude. When the
pack opened somewhat, Baffin decided to leave the
land and sail west, a voyage considered extremely
dangerous even by the well-found steam whalers of
this century. Navigating successfully the loose ice
pack of the "Middle Passage" of Melville Bay, he
reached July 1 an open sea, the "North Water"
of the whalers. Pushing yet northward beyond
capes York, Atholl and Parry, he was obliged to
turn back on July 5, when in sight of Cape Alexander. His latitude, about 77° 45' N., remained
unequaled in that sea for two hundred and thirty-
six years.

In quaint language, Baffin says that he was
forced by ice "to stand backe some eight leagues to
an island we called Hakluits Ile-it lyeth betweene
two great Sounds, the one Whale Sound, and the
other Sir Thomas Smith's Sound; this last runneth
to the north of 78°, and is admirable in one respect,
because in it is the greatest variation of the compasse
of the world known; for by divers good observations I found it to be above five points, or fifty-six
degrees varied to the westward."

A few days later Baffin turned southward, having
in this unsurpassed voyage sailed through ice-
packed seas more than three hundred miles farther

north than his able predecessor, John Davis.
Baffin thus added to geographical knowledge
Ellesmere and Prudhoe lands, and Baffin Bay with
its great radiating sounds of Smith, Jones and
Lancaster, — through the last named being the
long-sought route for a Northwest Passage. With
this voyage ended all efforts for three centuries to
discover a route via Davis Strait to Cathay and
the Indies.

For more than two hundred years the waters of
Baffin Bay were undisturbed by any keel. Moreover, the discoveries of Baffin faded from the minds
of men, and his own countrymen, through geographers, discredited the reports of this great
seaman, — William Baffin.

CHAPTER II

THE NORTHEAST PASSAGE

THE series of voyages in lower latitudes that followed the discovery of the New World by Columbus had their parallel during the following centuries in the persistent efforts of adventurous navigators to solve the problem of establishing communication with Cathay via the arctic seas.

A spirit of trade and commerce animated the original promoters of the search for either a Northeast or Northwest Passage, — a somewhat berated spirit which, nevertheless, is the basis of the material prosperity of the civilized nations. Desirous of participating in the great profits of the oriental trade carried on by their southern rivals, the enterprising merchants of England sought a northern route when debarred from the southern.

The European waters of the Northeast Passage must have been known by the Norse and Russian mariners from the earlier centuries, though the northern shore lines of the Scandinavian peninsula were not definitely mapped until 1539, reproduced by Olaus Magnus in "Historia de Gentibus Septentrionalibus," Rome, 1555. (See page 15.) Yet others had rounded the North Cape in the ninth century, and Istoma journeyed from the White Sea to Trondhjem in 1496.

This extended maritime venture by England, into unknown and distant seas, was viewed as an enterprise of unusual difficulty. The utmost care was exercised in preparations; ships were built specially suited to northern waters, the crews were selected men, and the outfitting was made by experts. The undertaking was recognized as a national enterprise, and the departure of the squadron of three ships, on May 30, 1553, under Sir Hugh Willoughby, was marked by salutes and other demonstrations of public enthusiasm in which the court and the populace equally participated. Nordenskiold points out that it was historic; he says, "All was joy and triumph, it seemed as if men foresaw that the greatest maritime power the history of the world can show, was that day born."

Willoughby and Derfouth perished with their crews on the coast of Lapland, but Chancellor extended Britain's trade, not with China but through Russia. (See Chapter XV.) The voyage of Burrough, 1556, reached the Petchora, and brought information as to Novaya Zemlya and of the Russian mariners' fishing and sailing as far as the Ob. Such intelligence not only seemed to forecast success, but international complications demanded further attempts.

In 1580 Philip II endeavored to ensure a con-

ARCTIC EUROPE WHEN NORTHWEST VOYAGES BEGAN.
OLAUS MAGNUS, ROME 1555

tinuance of the Spanish monopoly in the profitable trade with the Orient, and adopted methods calculated to eliminate the northern nations of Europe from such trade operations. His arrogance was such that in 1584 he issued a decree prohibiting the Netherlands from even trading with Portugal.

In this contingency, during 1580, Pet in the *George* and Jackman in the *William* — both tiny, ill-found barks — entered the mouth of the Petchora. They were the first vessels from western Europe that were ever navigated through the ice-encumbered Kara Sea. This terminated England's success in these explorations, for the voyage of Wood and Flaws in 1666 ended in shipwreck on Novaya Zemlya. The Dutch efforts in the three voyages of Barents, 1594–1597 (See Chapter XV), made no further progress, and efforts ended.

It remained for Sweden in the nineteenth century not only to prove the practicability of navigation, in normal years, through the Siberian Ocean, but also to be the first to make the voyage from the Atlantic to the Pacific Ocean through arctic waters. Through the support of Oscar Dickson and Alexander Sibiriakoff the navigability of Kara Sea was demonstrated, as urged by Adolf Erik Nordenskiold. With Kjellman in command, Nordenskiold reached the mouth of the Yenisei, August 15, 1875, after extended researches en route; the *Proven* returned the same season, reaching Tromsoe in the autumn. The voyage was repeated successfully in 1876, to and from the Yenisei.

Not content with his success in inaugurating a sea route of incalculable value for the development of Northern Asia, Nordenskiold addressed the Swedish Government in a memorial setting forth the practicability of a voyage from the Yenisei to Bering Strait, and the important results, material and scientific, that would result therefrom. His arguments were convincing. The cost of the voyage, $100,000, was in large part met by Dickson, who gave $60,000, King Oscar and Sibiriakoff, who subscribed $11,000 each. The Swedish Diet voted grants for equipping and provisioning the *Vega*. Captain L. Palander commanded, while Nordenskiold selected the scientific staff. The *Vega* left Tromsoe July 21, 1878, with the *Lena* to support her; the *Express* with coal supply, and the *Frazier* with a cargo for the Yenisei.

Finding the Kara Sea ice free, the coal was transferred, while the staff made scientific researches. Port Dickson was reached August 9, and the *Vega* and *Lena* steamed onward, while their consorts ascended the Yenisei. From the northernmost point, Cape Chelyuskin, the *Lena* was sent back on August 19. When within a day's steaming of Bering Strait, the *Vega* was beset by new ice, and was obliged to winter in Kolyutchin Bay. Both there, as well as at all other points touched on the coast, Nordenskiold and his staff made comprehensive collections, and wherever there were natives ethnological researches.

On July 18, 1879, the ice broke up and two days later the *Vega* steamed into Bering Strait (Nordenskiold: "The Voyage of the *Vega*." 1882). The story of this remarkable achievement was related by its initiator with a wealth of information that won the plaudits of all scientists.

CHAPTER III

THE NORTHWEST PASSAGE AND THE FRANKLIN SEARCH

As related in Chapter I, the efforts to discover a passage to Cathay via the arctic seas ended with the voyage of Baffin in 1616. It is significant of the modern spirit of adventure that the Northwest Passage should be sought again in the eighteenth century, and be discovered in the nineteenth century by a remarkable series of voyages, which brought to man's knowledge the existence of Arctic America.

In the middle of the eighteenth century, it became known that the last voyage of Bering (made in 1741) disclosed that the continents of America and Asia were separated by a strait, as related in Chapter IV. This discovery excited anew the activities of Great Britain in quest of the forgotten arctic route from the Atlantic to the Pacific. The attempt to circumnavigate North America was entrusted to the great navigator, James Cook, who decided to attack the problem through Bering Strait. His selection of this route is doubtless explained, when, speaking of Bering's voyages, he said, "His misfortunes proved to be the source of much private advantage to individuals,

[19]

and of public utility to the Russian nation." Cook's arctic voyage of 1778 added much to the knowledge of the northern coasts, but he failed to reach even Point Barrow and contributed nothing to the Passage.

In 1818 Great Britain felt called on to demonstrate her claim to be mistress of the seas, doubtless having in mind the activities of Kotzebue, 1816, north of Bering Sea, and of the successes of Scoresby in the Greenland Sea. The attempt to reach Bering Strait from Davis Strait was made by John Ross, in the *Isabella*, supported by Parry in the *Alexander*, in 1818, but he failed to add any new data about the region beyond the discovery of the Eskimos near Cape York, to whom he gave the fanciful name of Arctic Highlanders.

Dissatisfaction with Ross was so great that another expedition was sent in 1819, with orders to find the Northwest Passage. William Edward Parry, in the *Hecla*, was assisted by Liddon in the *Griper;* the voyage was very successful. Discovering and navigating Lancaster Sound, Barrow Strait, Melville Sound, Parry entered MacClure Strait, and after wintering on Melville Island, succeeded in proceeding westward in 1820 to 113° 48′ W. longitude, barely missing the attainment of Beaufort Sea and the completion of the task assigned him. However, he earned the reward of £5,000 offered by Parliament to any explorer who should pass the 110th meridian west of Greenwich.

The two ships returned safely to England that autumn.

The discoveries of the expedition were very extensive, covering nearly every one of the large arctic islands, and important, as it had passed to the north of the magnetic pole. His second expedition, 1821–1823, was a failure as regarded the Passage. However, he added new islands, found native tribes and explored the adjacent country from his two winterings; first in 66° 32′ N., 84° W., at Melville Peninsula, and then at Igloolik, 69° 22′ N. at the entrance to Fury and Hecla Strait. The final voyage of Parry, when he wintered in 1824–1825 at Port Bowen, 73° 12′ N., was without results. The experiences of Lyon, in the *Griper* (1824), were likewise fruitless, at Repulse Bay.

While it contributed nothing towards the discovery of the Northwest Passage, the expedition of John Ross, 1829–1833, was unique in experiences and results. Boothia Land, the northernmost point of the continent of America, was discovered and adjacent regions explored. From the ship's anchorage in Felix Harbor, 69° 59′ N., 92° W., James C. Ross, by extended observations in the field, located the north magnetic pole on the west coast of Boothia Land, in 70° 05′ N., 96° 44′ W. Amundsen relocated it near King William Land, in 1904.

The foregoing attempts were a prelude to the famous expedition of Sir John Franklin, which,

[21]

with the score of relief voyages, led eventually to the discovery of two navigable routes between Baffin Bay and Bering Strait. Franklin, in the *Erebus*, supported by Crozier in the *Terror*, sailed May 26, 1845, with one hundred and twenty-nine souls. Proceeding through Lancaster Sound, the expedition wintered, 1845–1846, at Beechey Island, 74° 43′ N., 91° 39′ W., where three seamen died and were buried. The following spring the squadron sailed south through Peel Sound into Franklin Strait, where both ships were beset, on September 12, 1846, north of King William Land, in 70° 05′ N., 98° 23′ W. Franklin died June 11, 1847. Drifting nineteen miles to the southwest, the ships were abandoned in Victoria Strait, adjacent to and in sight of the entrance to Dease Strait, and so had unconsciously completed the discovery of a navigable waterway to the Pacific, along the coast of North America.

The history of the Franklin expedition appears in the following records, obtained by McClintock in his memorable voyage of 1857–1859.[1] The Gore record, deposited on King William Land, reads thus :

28th of May, 1847. H. M. ships *Erebus* and *Terror* wintered in the ice, in latitude 70° 05′ N., longitude 98° 23′ W.

Having wintered in 1846–1847 [Error: should be

[1] McClintock: "Fate of Sir John Franklin;" "Voyage of the *Fox*." 5th ed. 1881.

CAPTAIN JOHN FRANKLIN, R. N.

Reproduced from an engraving of a painting by J. Jackson, R. A., and
published by John Murray, London, 1828.

1845–1846] at Beechey Island, in latitude 74° 43′ 28″ N., longitude 91° 39′ 15″ W., after having ascended Wellington Channel to latitude 77°, and returned by the west side of Cornwallis Island. Sir John Franklin commanding the expedition. All well. Party consisting of 2 officers and 6 men left the ships on Monday, 24th May, 1847.

> Gm. Gore, Lieut.
> Chas. F. Des Vœux, Mate.

On the margin of the record left by Gore the following was written :

April 25, 1848. H. M. Ships *Terror* and *Erebus* were deserted on the 22d of April, 5 leagues N.N.W. of this, having been beset since 12th September, 1846. The officers and crews, consisting of 105 souls, under the command of Capt. F. R. M. Crozier, landed in latitude 69° 37′ 42″ N., longitude 98° 41′ W. This paper was found by Lt. Irving, under the cairn supposed to have been built by Sir James Ross, 1831, 4 miles to the northward, where it had been deposited by the late Commander Gore, in June, 1847. Sir James Ross' pillar has not, however, been found; and the paper has been transferred to this position, which is that in which Sir James Ross' pillar was erected. Sir John Franklin died on the 11th of June, 1847, and the total loss by death in the Expedition has been to this date 9 officers and 15 men.

> F. R. M. Crozier, Captain and senior officer.
> James Fitzjames, Captain H.M.S. *Erebus*.

And start on tomorrow, 26th, for Back's Fish River.

By graves and skeletons the line of retreat is traced from Point Victory to Todd Island, south of King William Land, and there are reasons to believe that some reached Point Ogle and others Montreal Island; but with one and all it was death by disease, or worse — by starvation. That they met death with courage, loyalty and solidarity is indisputable. The old Eskimo woman paid the highest tribute possible to her ideal, that of physical merit, when she said to McClintock: "They fell down and died as they walked," a statement verified by the position of a skeleton found by McClintock himself. Faithful to the last, these heroic men, as Sir John Richardson beautifully says, "forged the last link of the Northwest Passage with their lives."

Before Franklin's fate was known, Great Britain sent forth about a score of expeditions, by land and by sea, for the relief of the lost explorers. The north coasts of Canada were explored by Richardson, without result (Richardson: "Boat Journey through Rupert Land"), and by John Rae, who was more successful, 1853–1854. Rae met on Boothia Land a young Eskimo who gave information as to the fate of the Franklin expedition, which was reënforced by the production of silver with the Franklin crest and other confirmatory articles (Rae: "Expedition to the Arctic Sea." 1850. Also undated *Blue Book*, 1855, 958 pp. and 26 maps). For this information the British Admiralty awarded to Rae and his companions £10,000, the offered reward for settling the fate of Franklin.

Extraordinary exertions were made by Great Britain in its searching expeditions by sea. For full information reference should be made to British *Blue Books:* March 7, 1850; December 20, 1852; undated Book, 1852, 216 pp. and 3 maps; undated Book 1854, 225 pp., 5 maps; undated Book, 1855, 958 pp., 26 maps. These expeditions were: Sir James Ross, *Investigator* and *Enterprise*, a conspicuous failure; — 1851–1852, Austin's squadron; Ommaney, *Assistance;* Osborn, *Intrepid;* Cator, *Pioneer;* United States ships: De Haven, *Advance*, and Griffin, *Rescue*, with Kane as surgeon. Private vessels were: Sir John Ross, *Felix;* Forsyth, *Prince Albert;* Penny, *Lady Franklin;* and Stewart, *Sophia*. Extended field work was done, and a few islands discovered. The only information concerning Franklin was made by Ommaney, who found on Beechey Island, August 23, 1851, three graves of men who had died on the *Erebus* and *Terror;* they had died between January and April, 1846; an exhaustive search disclosed no record.

The Arctic Committee caused to be despatched in 1852 a large squadron under Sir Edward Belcher (Belcher: "Last of Arctic Voyages." 2 vols. 1855). His ships were: Richards, *Assistance;* Kellett, *Resolute;* Osborn, *Pioneer;* McClintock, *Intrepid;* and Pullen, *North Star*. The activities and sledge

journeys of the squadron were unprecedented in
arctic history. The field travel exceeded 6,000
miles, as follows: Pim, 635 miles; Domville, 739;
Hamilton, 974; Nares, 980; Mecham, 1,163;
and McClintock, 1,401 miles. No signs of the
lost explorers were found. The notable accomplishment was the trip of Pim, which saved the
crew of the *Investigator*, in Mercy Bay. Belcher
abandoned the *Resolute*, the *Assistance*, *Enterprise*
and *Pioneer*, which were icebound, and returned to
England.

The search via Bering Strait, 1848–1854, began
under Moore, in the *Plover*, assisted by Kellett, in
the *Herald;* it had no outcome as regards Franklin.
The second squadron, sent forth in 1850, was composed of Collinson in the *Enterprise*, with M'Clure
in *Investigator*. M'Clure, contrary to positive
orders, separated from Collinson. Sailing northward, M'Clure discovered Banks Island and the
straits of Prince of Wales and M'Clure. Eventually, while attempting night navigation, the
Investigator grounded at the entrance to Mercy
Bay, Banks Island, 74° N., 118′ W., on September
23, 1851. In the spring of 1853, after having been
frozen in for eighteen months, conditions had
become so desperate M'Clure found it necessary
to abandon his ship. Game had become scarce,
supplies were nearly gone, half the crew were
helpless, and three had died in "early April a
week before their proposed departure on a forlorn

hope." On April 3, Bedford Pim, with a sledge party from Belcher's squadron, wintering to the east, visited Mercy Bay, and the crew was saved. Later under Belcher's orders the *Investigator* was abandoned, and its crew, crossing by sledge the ice of Melville Sound, was the first party to make the Northwest Passage.

The voyage of Collinson is one of the most remarkable and successful in arctic records. He sailed the *Enterprise* more then ten degrees of longitude through the narrow straits along the northern shores of continental North America, which never before or since have been navigated, save by small boats and with excessive difficulty. He searched all adjacent lands, and of all the governmental naval expeditions searching for Franklin, he came nearest the goal.

Following the continental coast of America, navigating safely the isle-bestrewed Coronation Gulf, Collinson passed east of Dease Strait and went into winter quarters at Cambridge Bay on September 28, 1852, in 69° N., 105° W. By sledge travel he searched the southeast coast of Victoria Land, his farthest point being Gateshead Island, 70° 26′ N., 101° W. Here he was on the historic strait in whose waters near by had sunk the abandoned *Erebus* and *Terror*. To the eastward within his vision was King William Land, where lay the unburied skeletons of the men he sought. He was unconscious that he and Franklin had by ship made

[27]

the Northwest Passage, which had been sought in vain for three centuries.

Collinson from two sources obtained traces of Franklin. The natives of Cambridge Bay had a steam-engine rod, and an article marked with the Queen's broad arrow, but having no interpreter — taken by M'Clure — he could not learn whence it came. On Finlayson Island Collinson also found part of a ship's door or hatchway, doubtless from one of Franklin's ships (Collinson : "Journal of *H.M.S. Enterprise.*" 1889).

When the British Government declined to prosecute the search further, Lady Franklin insisted on learning details. Fortunately she secured the coöperation of Leopold McClintock, who sailed in the *Fox*, July 1, 1857, with Allen Young and W. R. Hobson as assistants. Beset in Melville Bay, the *Fox* drifted eight months, one thousand two hundred miles to the south. Refitting in Greenland, in 1858, McClintock visited Beechey Island, and later wintered in Port Kennedy, 72° N., 94° W. Starting February 17, 1859, in a temperature sixty degrees below freezing, McClintock, in a journey of three hundred and sixty miles, gained results. He found forty-five Boothians well provided with relics of a party (Franklin) of "white people (who) starved upon an island (Montreal), where there is a river (Back)." He also practically completed the coast line of continental North America, and added one hundred and ten miles of unknown lands to the charts.

Back on sledge journey in April, McClintock and Hobson met natives from whom they bought Franklin relics. They said: Two ships had been seen near King William Land; one sank and the other was forced on shore by ice and broke up; the ships were destroyed in the autumn, and all the white people, taking boats, went away to the large river, and the following winter their bones were found there.

On May 7, near Port Parry, forty Eskimo were met, who sold them silver relics. They said the ship had disappeared; many books had been destroyed by the weather; and the wreck was last visited in the winter of 1858–1859. An old woman added that many of the men perished on Back River; some were buried, others not. On May 25, McClintock, on King William Land, came upon a bleached human skeleton lying on its face, in a position which indicated that the man, suffering from exhaustion, had fallen and died in that posture, thus confirming the truth of the words of the old Eskimo woman, who said, "They fell down and died as they walked."

In Erebus Bay, Hobson discovered a boat on a sledge, in which were two human skeletons, with a large quantity of clothing, and no food except forty pounds of chocolate and a little tea. At Point Victoria, Hobson found the record (already

[29]

reproduced), the first and last direct information that has ever been found (McClintock: "The Voyage of the *Fox*." 5th ed., London, 1881).

Young in 1875 attempted the Northwest Passage on the *Pandora*, but met an impassable barrier in Peel Strait, 72° 14′ N. (Young: The "Two Voyages of the *Pandora*." 1879).

It remained for Amundsen, in the twentieth century, to make the Passage, in the *Gjoa*. Leaving Norway in 1903, after extensive observations on King William Land to determine the exact position of the north magnetic pole, he sailed west in 1905, and in August reached Kings Point, 69° 10′ N., 138° W. Thus was solved another problem, and an added laurel was gained by a Scandinavian mariner.

CHAPTER IV

BERING SEA AND ITS ISLANDS

THE surfaces of the arctic regions are to a much greater extent water than land. In some places more than two miles deep, its ocean is nearly two thousand miles long and one thousand miles broad. From Point Barrow, Alaska, to North Cape, Norway, a distance of more than three thousand miles, there is no known land. This extensive, land-enclosed sea, with an area of nearly two million square miles, is in the main unnavigable, owing to its being continually covered by densely packed ice floes, some of great extent and thickness.

Its water connections with the North Atlantic Ocean are shallow passages, whose submarine ridges, rising to within two hundred and fifty fathoms of the surface, permit a quite insignificant outflow. Of these outlets only one is of extent and importance, that between Svalbard (Spitsbergen) and Greenland. Through this passage pours into the Atlantic continuously an ice stream of incalculable magnitude, skirting the east coast of Greenland. Minor and unimportant outflows occur between ice-clad Northeast Land and Franz Josef archipelago, as well as from Kara Sea to the

[31]

north of Novaya Zemlya, and from Baffin Bay. Extremely insignificant is the outflow through Bering Strait, which connects the Arctic Ocean with Bering Sea.

Various expeditions — Kotzebue, 1815–1818; Beechey, 1826; Seeman, 1853, and Rodgers, 1855 — contributed important observations relative to the hydrography of Bering Strait. However, it remained for William H. Dall — the well-known authority on Alaska, to settle a number of mooted questions, by making an exhaustive survey of Bering Strait. During 1871–1874, the U. S. Coast Survey work in Bering Sea, under Dall, comprised many thousand observations of current and temperature. It also established a series of magnetic stations from Sitka west to the Aleutian chain, which not only demonstrated the fact that the secular change of the magnetic declination had reached its eastern elongation, but had materially receded from the values determined by Rodgers in 1855.

In 1880 Dall supplemented these observations by a new series at suitable points in Bering Sea and Strait, and northward to Point Belcher, which confirmed conclusions previously reached. A hydrothermal survey of Bering Strait was made by serial temperatures every five fathoms at intervals of four miles, from Cape Prince of Wales to East Cape. This survey disclosed that the highest temperature of 48° near the American coast fell gradually to 36° near the coast of Asia. Hydrographic observations (taken in connection with those made north and south of the strait) disclosed that the principal current in Bering Strait is tidal and intermittent; that the warmth of the water is due to the warming up by the sun of the shallow waters of Kotzebue and Norton sounds, and not to a warm current from the southern part of Bering Sea; that the water south of St. Lawrence Island, in Bering Sea, is constantly colder than that on the eastern side of the strait; and finally, that the chief current of Bering Sea and Strait is a feeble but somewhat general movement of cold arctic water southward.

The hypothetical branch of the Japan current, which had long been supposed to enter Bering Sea and extend through the strait into the Arctic Ocean, was conclusively shown to have no actual existence, and the fact that the current in the strait runs northward with the flood and southeastward with the ebb tide was demonstrated by the observations.

EXPLORATIONS OF THE REGION

Vitus Bering discovered neither the sea nor the strait which bears his name, and left unsolved the important geographical problem as to the separation of America and Asia. The first passage of Bering Strait was the outcome of commercial enterprises, being the result of the efforts of the

Russian traders at the mouth of the Kolyma River to extend eastward their trading operations with the natives. In 1646 Isai Ignatief made a successful voyage to the east of the Kolyma, and initiated trade for walrus ivory with the Chuckches. The following voyage of Simon Deshnef to reach the reputed Anadyr River was unsuccessful.

In 1648 renewed efforts were made, and a squadron of seven vessels left Kolyma. Three only, under Deshnef, Alexief and Ankudinof, were able to make the long voyage. Fortunately the sea was ice-free, and rounding successfully the northeasterly cape of Asia they passed into Bering Strait. Disasters there awaited them, from which all perished — except Deshnef and his crew — from disease, encounters with hostile natives and shipwreck. Deshnef's vessel was wrecked on the coast of Kamchatka, south of Anadyr Bay. Supporting themselves by the chase on the banks of the Anadyr during the winter, the crew ascended the stream the following spring. They built there the post of Anadyrsk, the first settlement of civilized men in the Bering Sea region. Traditionally, in 1654, a trader named Stadukin, circumnavigating northeastern Asia, reached the Kurile Islands.

In 1711, Popof visited East Cape to exact tribute from the Chuckches; he brought back an account of new islands (Diomedes), and reported that there was a continent not far to the eastward. This report of the contiguity of America eventually led to a government expedition to verify the report.

The voyages of Vitus Bering were due to the decision of that masterful Russian, Peter the Great, who in the last year of his eventful life planned one of the greatest geographical expeditions ever recorded. It was known as the Great Northern Expedition, and was carried out after the death of Peter. It entailed seventeen years (1725–1742) of efforts on the part of various explorers, and is said to have impoverished many tribes of natives by its heavy exactions of supplies and unceasing demands for transportation. The series of journeys and voyages that explored the north coasts of Siberia, which are recorded in Chapter XVII, were supplementary to those here mentioned.

The expedition under Bering, a Dane in the service of Russia, left St. Petersburg February 4, 1725. His journey across Siberia, the accumulation of supplies and construction of a vessel at Okhotsk, involved almost insuperable efforts and innumerable delays. The initial voyage was made by his assistant, Spanberg, who sailed in the summer of 1727 across the sea of Kamchatka to Bolsheretsk. Another year was there passed in building the second ship.

Finally, after preparations covering three years and four months, Bering sailed on July 24, 1728, on a voyage of exploration that lasted seven weeks

only. Coasting northward, he met in the Anadyr
Gulf a party of Chuckches navigating its waters.
They told him that to the northeast the land
changed its direction to the north and west.

Pursuing his voyage he came to an island, which
he named St. Lawrence in honor of his patron
saint. East Cape was passed August 26, and the
Asiatic shore was skirted to the neighborhood of
67° 18′ N., 170° W. From this point Bering
turned back, as he says, "because the land no longer
extended north. Neither from the Chuckche
coast *nor to the eastward could any extension of land
be observed*. If we should continue on our course
and happen to have contrary winds, we could not
get back to Kamchatka before the close of navigation." Chaplin, his lieutenant, reported that
Bering turned back "in spite of his instructions."
In any event this voyage added nothing to the
discoveries of Deshnef, a century earlier, since
Bering's quoted words indicate clearly that the
American continent to the eastward was not seen,
though some of his apologists have advanced a
contrary opinion. Another feeble attempt at
exploration was made to reach land to the eastward, said to be visible on fine days, in the summer
of 1729. After a voyage of less than three days
he abandoned the search, and made his way as
speedily as possible overland to St. Petersburg,
where he arrived March 15, 1730.

Bering had been absent five years, and had

utterly failed as to the essential object of his mission, to determine whether or not the continents of America and Asia were there separated. Despite criticisms, the Empress Anne gave orders for a second expedition on a more extended scale, under his command. In the spring of 1733 Bering left St. Petersburg with Spanberg and other officers. Assigned to the specific duty of making discoveries to the southward, Spanberg sailed from Kamchatka in 1739, and extended his explorations along the Kurile Islands to Japan.

It was not until September, 1740, seven years after his second departure from St. Petersburg, that Bering with Tschirikof left Okhotsk, and instead of taking to the open sea proceeded to Avatcha, now Petropavlovsk, where he wintered. Finally, on June 15, 1741, Bering sailed from Petropavlovsk in the *St. Peter*, with Lieutenant Waxel and physicist William Steller. Tschirikof in the *St. Paul* had as astronomer De la Croyere. Time was wasted searching for the mythical land of Gama, and then the ships parted in foggy weather.

Tschirikof sailed northeast and reached, July 26, the Alaskan coast near Cross Bay. Unable to make a safe harbor, and seeing natives in canoes, he decided to examine the shore by landing parties. Dementief with ten men, and Safelef with three men, landed, between July 29 and August 4 ; no man of either party was seen again and their fate is conjectural. Tschirikof followed the Alaskan coast more than one hundred miles and saw at one time twenty-one natives, each man in a kayak (skin boat). Lack of water and proper food caused outbreaks of scurvy, from which both of his lieutenants and some of his crew died. These conditions caused him to return and Tschirikof safely reached Petropavlovsk, October 21, 1741, De la Croyere dying the same day.

These explorations were duplicated by Bering, who reached on July 29 the Alaskan coast, between capes St. Elias and St. Hermogenes. During his stay of three days, for water, his landing party discovered freshly cooked food. Stellar criticised Bering for ordering immediate departure, an action fully justified by the fate of the crew of the *St. Paul*, mentioned above. Following the coast westward, he discovered coastwise islands, and obtained water at an island named Shumagin for a sailor he buried there. Natives were met at sea, but relations with them were avoided. Later, a violent storm of seventeen days left the party in bad condition, short of provisions with two thirds of the crew unfit for duty. On November 15 the *St. Peter* was in 56° N. latitude, and the next day stranded on a shoal (of Bering Island) and speedily broke to pieces. Fortunately the crew reached shore, and yet more fortunately the wreck was driven up so that its timbers furnished material for a boat, in which the survivors escaped to the mainland in the spring of 1742.

Alaska Division, U. S. Bureau of Education

TEACHERS AND NATIVES ON ST. LAWRENCE ISLAND. OLD-STYLE ESKIMO SKIN-COVERED HUT IN FOREGROUND; MODERN HOUSE IN BACKGROUND.

Alaska Division, U. S. Bureau of Education

ESKIMO WOMEN AND CHILDREN ON ST. LAWRENCE ISLAND, NEAR ENTRANCE TO BERING STRAIT.

Already sick, Bering was now utterly discouraged, and refusing food and shelter died on December 19, 1741.

Waxel says: "We younger persons recovered our spirits, took courage, resolved to do our utmost, and leave no means untried to save our lives." The resolution and skill of this young officer, on whom the command now devolved, secured the safety of the party. He was ably seconded by the professional efforts of Doctor Steller, whose industry and cheerfulness were unbounded, under conditions where "Want, nakedness, frost, rain, impatience and despair were our companions."

Steller's work as a naturalist was pursued, and his observations under untoward conditions were most valuable contributions, relating as they do to the extinct sea-cow and other sea animals formerly closely hunted. Persecuted by jealous officials, he perished miserably in Siberian wilds at 37. Leonard Stejneger, in the American expedition of 1882–1883, to Commander (Bering) Island, thoroughly explored the fauna and flora of this region.

Although Bering discovered neither strait nor sea, Bering's voyages were fruitful in geographic and commercial results. Not only were they of utility to Russia but in the twentieth century have proved to be of vast material value. The wintering at Bering Island led to the exploitation of the region by hunters, and to the occupation and exploitation of Alaska.

[39]

MATERIAL CONTRIBUTIONS OF BERING SEA

The amount of wealth drawn by Russians from Bering Sea before the cession of Alaska is unknown, but it must have aggregated in the neighborhood of one hundred million dollars. Confined almost entirely to the furry products of sea and land, the most prolific sources of profit to the Russians in Alaska were the fur seal, walruses, sea otters, foxes and beavers.

The most important industry of the United States is the control of the otary or fur-seals' herds, on the fur-seal reservation of the Pribilof Islands. The gross receipts therefrom were approximately $60,000,000, including 1927. The herd in 1927 numbered 761,281 animals, from which in 1926 there were taken 22,131 pelts. The value of the furs varies slightly from year to year; in 1926 it was about $750,000. Furs from foxes trapped on this reservation amount to nearly $25,000 annually. The whaling catch was valued at $625,-000 in 1925, and $680,000 in 1926. The salmon caught in these waters must run into the millions each year. The products of this region are therefore of importance to the nations of the earth.

ASIATIC NATIVES OF THE REGION

There are two classes of natives, the reindeer Chuckches and the coast Chuckches. The reindeer natives live by deer-raising and trade,

[40]

wandering between the Indigirka and the sea. The coast natives live a half-nomadic, half-settled existence along the Asiatic shore. The Chuckches seem to be the only Siberian natives that had the moral force and physical bravery to withstand the tribute exactions of Russian officials and traders. Schestakof, 1730, and Pavlutski, 1731, failed in their costly efforts to enforce tribute. Contact with traders and officials in the twentieth century has made great changes in the lives of these and other Asiatic natives. For their customs and life conditions in former years, an excellent account is given by Kennan in his "Tent Life in Siberia", revised edition, 1910.

AMERICAN NATIVES

These are principally descendants from offshoots of the Siberian tribes. Of present importance are those entirely under governmental control on the Pribilof Reservation, and the independent Eskimos of Nunivak and of St. Lawrence Island. In each case families of nomadic, irresponsible hunters have been transformed into coördinated communities performing useful labor, living peaceful and comfortable lives.

Most phenomenal is the evolution wrought in the conditions at St. Lawrence Island. This island lies in about 63° N., at the southern entrance to Bering Strait. For eight months in the year it is icebound, and cannot be reached by ship. In winter Bering Sea is frozen across to Siberia, and after a heavy gale the coast of the island is covered by heavy ice masses, with hummocks piled up as high as thirty feet. On its bleak, treeless hills and in its *tundra,* or frozen marshes, appear scanty forms of vegetation, — dwarf willows, shrubs, arctic grasses and reindeer moss. An unattractive environment, which the natives occupied when unable to seek their food in the sea.

Neglected and uncared for by the Federal Government, despite obligations assumed in the treaty of cession, these Siberian Eskimo steadily degenerated. The result of thirteen years of neglect is set forth by Petroff, in his census report of 1880. He said: "This island originally had a population of about 1,000, but during the winter of 1878, on account of the failure to lay in supplies during the hunting season, a period of general starvation occurred, which caused the deaths of at least 400 men, women and children. . . . Living directly in the track of vessels bound to the Arctic for the purpose of whaling and trading, this situation has been a curse to them; for as long as the rum lasts they do nothing but drink."

Hooper in the *Corwin* visited the island the next summer. He reported: "The original settlement had been near the water, on a slightly elevated flat, but during the famine all the inhabitants died, with the exception of those now occupying the two houses on the hill, about sixteen in number. . . .

Near one of the houses, I counted eight empty whisky casks."

Urged by the Army, missionary work in Alaska was commenced by Jackson in 1877, but Congress did nothing until, stirred by popular criticism, it finally made a pitifully inadequate appropriation of $25,000 for the "needful and proper provision for the education of the children in Alaska without reference to race." No dollar was spent for medicine or to prevent starvation, until Secretary Hitchcock, on the recommendation of General Greely, made an allotment in 1906 for alleviating the sufferings of the sick and to save natives from starving.

However, in 1894, when the population of St. Lawrence Island had increased to about two hundred, the Bureau of Education sent Mr. and Mrs. Gambell to begin the education of the natives. Their effective work came to an end when they perished by shipwreck in 1898. For them the principal village is named Gambell. In 1894 the Eskimo were dishonest, unreliable, quarrelsome, given to drink, lived in filthy huts, and were afflicted with diseases.

After more than thirty years of unremitting care and practical instruction by the agents of the Bureau of Education, these natives have become useful and law abiding. They are reliable, non-drinkers, peaceable and laborious. In Gambell there are three Eskimo stores, one coöperative.

[43]

Thirty-one families live in wooden houses, under sanitary conditions. Many of the comforts and conveniences of civilized life have been introduced. Hunting and fishing are facilitated by modern methods, in which fifteen large whaleboats supplement their skin canoes. The herd of reindeer introduced about twelve years ago have prospered, and their increase is a guarantee for food and clothing in seasons of bad fishing.

Under the Bureau of Fisheries the Pribilof natives have been safeguarded and improved in every respect. Medical, school and church facilities are provided. St. George is lighted by electricity, cement houses have been built and pure water introduced. Their condition is as a whole better than that of laborers in many civilized towns. The reindeer supplement their previous fish diet. Employed in the capture of seals, foxes and birds, in the curing of skins, they have steady and congenial work, for which they are well paid. Many of the natives have substantial savings, and some visit the United States for a higher education than is afforded by the local schools.

Reporting on the condition of a native settlement, remote and isolated, with few reindeer, having no commercial industries, a scientist says: "The Nunivakers, from the standpoint of physical, material and social culture, probably are the most primitive of all Alaskan Eskimo." Their environment explains their condition. The second largest island of the Bering Sea is Nunivak, its area being about three hundred square miles. Situated off the route of travel, near a rocky and dangerous coast, it is rarely visited, the nearest settlement being a hundred miles distant. The island is rocky, treeless, fog-enshrouded and wind-swept most of the year. There are about two hundred inhabitants, Eskimo untainted by any crossing with other races. For several years they have been under the care of teachers of the Bureau of Education. Intelligent, peaceful and industrious, they live principally on fish and seal seasoned with seaweeds, salmon and berries. Some show unusual mental qualities, expressed in songs and ditties about their life ; some do artistic work in carvings of arctic birds and animals. Their log huts are sunk well into the ground, making them nearly underground. In short they perpetuate in most respects the life methods of their ancestors in previous centuries. The reindeer introduced have increased rapidly, and by crossings with caribou — through the action of the Biological Survey — have become an improved breed that promises to to be of marked economic value.

The small band of natives on Little Diomede have materially improved under the teachers sent to the island by the Alaska Division of the Bureau of Education.

Thus Bering Sea and its natives are contributing to the material benefit of the nations of the earth.

CHAPTER V

ARCTIC ALASKA

For many reasons the material development of Arctic Alaska is worthy of consideration. It has been owned and governed by two great nations, and until the Twentieth Century no proper measures were adopted for the welfare of its native inhabitants. The Territory, however, has varied and extensive resources which have been economically profitable in the past, and are most promising for the future. In the exploitation of coal, copper, fur-bearing animals, fish, gold, lumber, oil, reindeer, silver, whales, seals and other marine animals, there have been drawn to the far north many thousands of men, whose activities have caused them to become residents. These settlements have extended poleward to Point Barrow, which is the northernmost village of continental America. While neglect on the part of the federal powers long threatened the decadence of all native tribes, a changed policy is gradually ensuring the primitive people conditions of peace and comfort, of education and prosperity far exceeding those of their ancestors.

The organization of the Russian-American

Trading Company in 1799 was the earliest step to bring about systematic relations between the native hunters and the Russian merchants. The development of Arctic Alaska began under Baron Wrangel, who was appointed Director in 1831. Under him were established the trading posts at St. Michael in 1831, and at Nulato in 1838. As the value of the northern fur trade became known, the Hudson's Bay Company encroached on the Russian territory, and sending its agents westward from the Mackenzie valley, established a trading post in 1847 at Fort Yukon, within the arctic zone. The cession of Alaska by Russia to the United States in 1867 led to the providing of transportation to this region. In 1869 the Alaska Commercial Company initiated steam navigation on the Yukon River.

EXPLORATIONS OF ARCTIC ALASKA

For convenience the regions to the north of the Yukon River — its northernmost waters being within the arctic zone — are here classed as Arctic Alaska. In 1767 Synd landed at Cape Prince of Wales, followed in 1778 by James Cook, in search of the Northwest Passage. This distinguished navigator was turned back by an impenetrable ice pack near Icy Cape, in 70° 41′ N. Later Cook explored Norton Sound, and, eliminating the mythical island of Alaschka, charted by Staehlin, visited the northwestern coast of America.

In 1816, Otto von Kotzebue reached Cape Krusenstern, 67° N., and discovered Kotzebue Sound, which he carefully surveyed (Kotzebue: "Voyage of Discovery", 1815–1818. 3 vols. 1821). Beechey, in 1826, reached in the Arctic Ocean 71° 08′ N., 163° 40′ W., and sent in a barge Elson, who succeeded in tracing the coast a distance of one hundred and twenty-six miles — from Icy Cape to Point Barrow. This point, in 71° 24′ N., is the most northerly land of North America, except Boothia Felix, which extends to 72° N.

The Franklin search expeditions — Kellett, Moore, Maguire, Collinson and M'Clure — contributed incidental knowledge of Alaska. Lt. John Rodgers, 1855, reaching 72° 05′ N., 174° 37′ W., eliminated Plover Land of Kellett; he also surpassed his predecessors in latitude.

The occupation of Alaska by Russia led to further explorations under Baron Wrangel, Director. An expedition to Norton Sound resulted in the establishment of a trading post on St. Michael Island in 1831, and exploration of the lower Yukon was followed by the opening of a similar station at Nulato. However, it was not until 1863 that the central course of the Yukon was known, when Lukeen ascended the river to Fort Yukon. In 1885 Lt. Henry Allen explored the Copper, Tanana and Koyukuk rivers. P. S. Smith, Geological Survey, in 1924–1926, explored on the arctic littoral the region in and adjacent to the Naval Petroleum Reserve. The International Polar station at Point Barrow is recorded in Chapter XX.

INHABITANTS OF ARCTIC ALASKA

The natives are either Athapascan or Eskimo. The Athapascans are a western offshoot of the tribes in the Mackenzie valley. They cover practically all the hunting grounds of the Yukon valley, except the delta region. Epidemics and famines have largely reduced their number, the census of 1920 recording a total of 4,697. They have contributed to the success of river navigation by becoming in considerable numbers laborers, woodmen and pilots. They do not profit by the federal schools as readily as other natives.

By the census of 1920 the Eskimos numbered 13,698 out of 26,558 natives. They inhabit the entire coast of the Arctic Ocean, and the eastern shores of Bering Sea from Norton Sound to Bristol Bay. Several thousand live in the delta regions of the Yukon and Kuskokwim. They have been quick to adopt such civilized methods as are applicable in their environment. They own about 400,000 reindeer; have established coöperative stores; entered into trade; have savings accounts; and have become a recognized economic factor of the nation. Having natural mechanical gifts, they enter the trades. Some become teachers, others enter the professions, and at Nome a journal is published by them, *The Eskimo*, with contributions in English.

MISSIONS

The first advance in the uplift of the natives was made by missions, initiated by Captain S. P. Jocelyn, U. S. Army. The labors of these self-sacrificing men and women, never fully appreciated, involved dangers of travel, endurance of rigorous climate, isolation, lack of medical care and civilized necessities. One, Doctor Sheldon Jackson, by persistent efforts enriched Arctic Alaska by the introduction of reindeer.

North of the Yukon missions maintained in 1927 were:

Catholic: Akularak, Koferesky (Holy Cross), Nulato.

Congregationalists: Kinegnak (Cape Prince of Wales), Shishmaref and Shishmaref Inlet.

Episcopal: Allakaket, Circle, Kaltag, Nome, Tanana and others.

Friends: Deering, Kikiktat (??Kiwalik) and Kotzebue.

Presbyterian: Point Barrow.

Norwegian Lutheran: Teller.

Swedish Lutheran: Golofin and Unalakleet.

The Baptists, Methodists and Moravians labored south of the Yukon.

EDUCATION

In late years education along practical lines has done much for northern Alaska. A dozen or more schools of whites and mixed races are maintained by the Territory, at an annual cost of $104 per capita.

The Federal Government ignored the natives until 1885, and for ten years made pitiful contributions, during which period thousands perished by famine and epidemics. Secretary Hitchcock of the Interior Department secured the coöperation of General A. W. Greely, who recommended in 1905 suspension of indiscriminate charity, which should be continued only in emergencies, in remote regions. Medical aid should be continued, conjoined with instruction in sanitary methods. To train the natives to self-help there should be introduced industrial training, suited to the different environments.

Along these lines the U. S. Bureau of Education has since worked, extending and improving as money became available. It was a difficult problem, dealing with six races, — Aleuts, Athapascans, Eskimos, Haidas, Tlinkits and Tsimpshians. Its personnel has faced ably questions of destitution, education, coöperation, segregation and economic thrift. Gradually industrial training has been introduced, locally and in vocational schools. Locally cleanliness, cooking, weaving, hygiene,

[51]

nursing and sanitation are taught and enforced.

Only such trades as environment needs demand are taught in the three vocational schools, — one of which, White Mountain, is in Arctic Alaska. These various trades include carpentry in several branches — such as boat, house and sled construction — blacksmithing, etc., marine engineering and navigation. Their efficient labors and instruction have materially improved the standards of native life and ambitions. There are few localities to-day where a healthy native adult is unable to be self-supporting, — that is, as to food, shelter and clothing. Medical care and education are the only outside matters of necessity. There are now native carpenters, engineers, preachers and teachers. Crimes are rare, divorces few, and illiteracy of natives under twenty-five years has fallen to thirty-four per cent.

In Arctic Alaska thirty-seven schools were in operation in 1927. The enrollment of 1,426 pupils included 1,174 Eskimo and 252 Athapascans. At White Mountain, Seward Peninsula, the advantages of the vocational school have been increased by the construction of a dormitory for the fifty-six Eskimos there enrolled.

Hospitals are almost entirely wanting, and the natives are dependent on what is termed the community service, rendered by the teachers, in connection with births, deaths, home visits and medical assistance. However, since the terrible epidemic of 1918, the number of native births has exceeded the deaths, in school districts, by 958.

INDUSTRIES AND TRADE

The contribution of Arctic Alaska to trade has been great in value and striking in variety; it plays no inconsiderable part in the products of the Territory. The shipments of entire Alaska in the past four years, 1924–1927, exceeded three hundred million dollars; those of 1927 aggregated $80,018,034, all Alaskan products.

Only about one sixth of their gold comes from Arctic Alaska, but another sixth comes from the adjacent regions, — the southern watershed of the Yukon. The production of the arctic regions depended upon the Seward Peninsula and the Kobuk valley. The output of the gold placers of Seward Peninsula — better known as Nome — has far exceeded $100,000,000, and its annual product promises steady increase. The introduction of steam dredges and other modern methods is adding to the production there which rose from $1,088,500 in 1925 to $1,873,000 in 1926.

The exploitation of furs from land animals, of reindeer and the whale fishery exceed in value the minerals. The pelts of land animals are increasing in number and value. Land furs have benefited Alaska to more than $30,000,000; in late years the shipments have increased from about $1,700,000

[53]

in 1923 to $2,349,640 in 1926. Of the shipments in 1926, Arctic Alaska contributed values of about $700,000; the furs from the extreme northwest division alone amounted to $483,000. The shore whaling industry on the arctic coast is a comparatively small affair, but the total value of the whale products in 1926 was $679,824 as against $631,959 the previous year. (See Greely: Handbook of Alaska, 1927.)

The reindeer numbered in 1927 more than 600,-000 head. In the northern regions are located thirty-seven of the fifty-three reindeer stations, and as they contain the largest herds, the deer in Arctic Alaska must number about 400,000. As two thirds of these are owned by the Eskimos, this newly acquired wealth has wrought great changes in their life-methods. Along the coasts of the Polar Ocean huts have been replaced by houses, camps by villages and barter by systematic trade. In short the nomadic, wandering hunters have been transformed into a stock-raising class, which has largely adopted civilized methods of life. Along this coast there are well populated villages — such as Barrow, Point Hope and Wainwright — with houses, schools, stores, motor boats, etc.

The reindeer industry is no longer local, as it has been commercialized by far-seeing men, who have incorporated at Nome. Selected animals are carefully slaughtered, stored in local refrigerating

Industrial Institution, U. S. Bureau of Education, Alaska

THREE ESKIMOS WORKING BAND SAW, JOINER, AND RIP SAW.

Alaska Division, U. S. Bureau of Education

ESKIMO VILLAGE OF WAINWRIGHT, ON COAST OF THE ARCTIC OCEAN.
LAST SOUTH-BOUND MAIL, MARCH 5.

plants, and moved along the coast in cold-storage boats. The amount marketed is steadily increasing, and the amount of meat used locally and in shipments far exceeds a million pounds annually; in 1927 there were shipped 990,000 pounds of reindeer meat to the United States.

North of the Yukon coal is present in fields of great extent, especially on the arctic coast between Cape Beaufort and Wainwright Inlet, and in regions adjacent to Point Barrow. Easily mined, now being procured by the Eskimos for local use, it is not improbable that in future years Alaska may furnish coal for the Pacific, as West Spitsbergen is now doing for northern Europe.

The possibility of petroleum deposits on the arctic coast is indicated by the withdrawal from private entry, in 1923, of 35,000 square miles, south of Point Barrow, known as Naval Petroleum Reserve Number 4.

The general impression that Arctic Alaska is a land of eternal frost and ice, unsuited for habitation and unsupplied with vegetation, is entirely incorrect. Agriculture is of limited extent, but barley, winter rye and winter wheat mature in selected places. North of the Yukon are many flourishing gardens, the best known being that at the Holy Cross Mission (Koserefyski), on the lower Yukon, where for thirty years potatoes and other hardy vegetables have rarely failed, while its dairy has always prospered. Even in the Koyukuk valley, as far as Coldfoot, 68° N., gardening is successful.

Opinions differ as to the lines on which Alaska will materially develop, but in any event there are in Arctic Alaska thousands of natives, who, previously nomadic and occasionally famine stricken, have become industrious and self-supporting communities, holding their own and growing in importance.

CHAPTER VI

POLAR CANADA

THE northern seacoast of America was first reached in 1771 by Samuel Hearne, who, in search of copper and to extend trade, attained the mouth of the Coppermine River. His successor, Alexander Mackenzie, reached the delta of the Mackenzie River in July, 1798. The tracing of the coast between these two isolated points was due to the energy of that great explorer, John Franklin, in two land journeys, 1819–1822 and 1825–1827 (Franklin: "First and Second Journey to the Shores of Polar Ocean." 1824 and 1828).

Under conditions of almost insuperable difficulties and of extreme hardships, with his indomitable assistants George Back and John Richardson, Franklin from his headquarters at Fort Enterprise, 64° 25′ N., 113° W., filled in the coast line from the Coppermine east to Dease Strait, in the expedition of 1819–1822. The explorations of 1825 were made from a station on Great Bear Lake. Richardson traced the unknown coast between the Mackenzie and the Coppermine. Franklin, working westward from the Mackenzie, followed the coast to Return Reef, 149° W. Thomas Simpson

("Discoveries on the North Coast of America."
1843) not only confirmed the discoveries of Franklin and Richardson, but filled in the shores west to
Point Barrow, and to King William Land to the
east.

Of geographic importance was the exploration
of the region of Great Fish (Back) River (Back:
"Arctic Land Expedition." 1836), and Rae's discovery that Boothia Felix is a part of the continent
(Rae: "Expedition to the Arctic Sea." 1850).

The coasts and regions thus made known through
the daring explorations of Mackenzie, Franklin
and Simpson, by broadening commercial and
industrial enterprises, have risen from their status
of worthless wastes to the dignity of regions contributory to the needs and desires of man.

THE ARCTIC DISTRICTS

The districts covered by this chapter include
those continental portions of the Dominion of
Canada which are governed by special administra-
tions. They are situated between the 60th parallel
to the south and the continental shores of the
Arctic Sea to the north, and their area is enormous,
about a million and a half square miles.

Formerly known as Rupert Land, it was dominated by a royal monopoly, the Hudson's Bay
Company, which, from its charter of 1670, were
"true and absolute lords and proprietors." Ex-
periencing certain modifications as to scope and

extent, their powers were not materially changed until the middle of the nineteenth century. In 1869 the Company transferred its rights to the Dominion of Canada for the sum of £300,000, retaining a large area of land, which in 1927 amounted to 2,872,000 acres. The Hudson's Bay Company still profits largely from its lands and the fur trade, the net income for all Canada in 1926–1927 being £151,909. It yet maintains more than forty trading stations and sub-stations in Arctic Canada.

The northern territory is divided into two provinces, the Yukon Territory and Northwest Territories. The Canadian arctic islands are treated in Chapter VII.

YUKON TERRITORY

This district lies in the main between Alaska to the west, and the watershed of the Mackenzie to the east; however, it includes the upper basin of Peel River. Its area slightly exceeds 200,000 square miles. Except along the coast of Beaufort Sea, it is a wooded country, containing aspen, birch, fir, pine, poplar and spruce. The upper tributaries of the Yukon and the Porcupine furnish cheap and extensive water transportation during the summer season.

The earliest explorations were made by the active agents of the Hudson's Bay Company between 1840 and 1850. Occupation began with the establishment of a trading post at Fort Yukon (in Alaska) in 1847, and another at Fort Selkirk, at the junction of the Pelly and Lewes rivers, in 1849; Selkirk was abandoned in 1852 after being captured and pillaged by the Chilkats of the Lynn Canal region. The fur trade continued to be the controlling industry for half a century until displaced by mineral exploitation.

Although minor amounts of gold were early obtained, the development of placer mining was due to McQuesten, who opened a trading station at Fort Reliance on the Yukon in 1874, near the site of Dawson. This became the rendezvous of the prospectors who began mining on Stewart River in 1885. Yukon mining was unimportant until Carmack in 1896 found the placers on Bonanza Creek followed by Henderson's discoveries on Gold Bottom, — both deposits of marvelous richness.

These discoveries attracted more than thirty thousand prospectors and camp followers, who, entering the Lynn Canal, reached the White Horse Rapids of Yukon River through the Chilkoot and other mountain passes. Thence by makeshift boats they reached the Klondike district.

Dawson, the capital of Yukon Territory, sprang up as a magic city; saloons and assay offices, schools and churches, libraries and hospitals, telephones and electric lights, newspapers and power plants. To efficiently meet the situation, an Act of the Canadian Parliament created Yukon a separate Territory, with official personnel for its good government. When the placers began to fail, the form of government was changed, and in 1927 it consisted of a gold commissioner appointed, and three councilmen elected. The Royal Mounted Police continue to maintain order and enforce the laws. The population, which once numbered between ten and fifteen thousand, was but 975 by the census of 1921, but is somewhat larger at present.

In 1924 there were 1,456 Indians, who lived quite prosperously as hunters; some raised potatoes and other hardy vegetables. For their children there were maintained in 1926 five schools with 192 pupils, at an expense of $16,932.

MINERAL PRODUCTION OF THE YUKON

The fur production of the Yukon fell rapidly when gold was found in paying quantities. The total mineral production of the territory to 1927 must approximate $250,000,000. Gold values alone to 1925 exceeded $181,000,000, as officially recorded, but large amounts escaped taxation. The output annually was more than $10,000,000 from 1898 to 1904, attaining a maximum in 1900 of $22,750,000. Then an almost unbroken decrease, due to the failure of the placers, ended with a product of $722,005 in 1924, followed, however, by $988,465 in 1925.

While placer gold is important, it is being largely

[61]

supplemented by the development of the silver-lead ores of Keno and the galena of the Mayo district, on the Stewart watershed. The silver output was $1,241,953 in 1923; $151,249 in 1924; and $624,-924 in 1925. Lead for the same years amounted to $486,008, $73,222 and $171,040.

Climatic and transportation difficulties — silver ores were originally sent for reduction to the United States — have been largely overcome by the construction of a local concentrator which greatly increases the output. The gold, silver and lead product of 1923–1925 averaged more than $1,900,-000 annually.

Water power is available, even in winter, for mining in the Mayo and Whitehorse districts. A hydro-electric plant, twenty-six miles from Dawson, furnishes that city with power, light, water and fire protection. Power for dredges is also transmitted thirty-five miles to Granville, and fifty-four miles to Little Twelvemile. Radios at Dawson and Mayo facilitate industry.

The fur trade, interrupted in the days of great gold production, has assumed better proportions and has led to the establishment of fur farms. The few farmers who have cattle, sheep and poultry are also adding fox-raising. The shipments of furs from the Yukon in the year 1925–1926 were valued at $320,808. The fish products in 1925 were worth $15,370, and would be largely increased if means of export were good.

THE NORTHWEST TERRITORIES

The area of these territories, islands included, exceeds 1,300,000 square miles, more than one third of the Dominion. It is governed by a commissioner, who exercises control through the Royal Canadian Mounted Police. The police administer justice in most cases, but trials for murder or very serious crimes are conducted by a stipendiary justice, detailed from the superior judges of the Dominion.

The only products are those resulting from the hunting and trapping on land, and from lake and sea fisheries. The population is slowly increasing, numbering in 1911, 6,507; in 1921, 7,988; and as estimated, 8,600 in 1925. The valley of the Mackenzie is by far the most important section.

THE MACKENZIE WATERSHED

This region, with an area of 682,000 square miles, is watered by the Mackenzie, one of the great rivers of the world. Its length, to the head of the Finla, is 2,525 miles. Its navigability for steamers is 1,400 miles, between Fort Smith and the Arctic Ocean. The northern timber limits closely approach the sea, being rarely one hundred miles distant from it. Hardy vegetables and winter grains grow in sheltered valleys as far north as the 63d parallel. From this region comes a considerable part of the enormous fur products

[63]

of Canada. Numerous large lakes exist, such as the Great Bear Lake (area 11,821 square miles) and Great Slave Lake (area 10,719), which are abundantly stocked with fine fish, and furnish yearly more than 500,000 pounds of food for local use.

It has naturally followed that these favorable conditions have led to industrial developments. The immediate river shores are most favorable for utilization from Fort Smith northward to the Mackenzie delta. The greater number of the 2,888 Indians in the Northwest Territories are located here. In the region of the great lakes there were living, as shown by the last census, 959 Dog Ribs, 731 Slaves, and 200 Yellowknives. There are more than forty trading posts, from Fort Smith at the extreme south to Aklavik at the mouth of the Mackenzie. Twelve settlements have post-offices. Aklavik is the center of the thriving trade on the arctic coast; Fort Smith is the trade metropolis of the watershed. Its radio is in communication with Aklavik, and its hospital cares for suffering natives. Besides an extensive trade, it builds motor and other boats for the Eskimos of the north and the Indians of the great lakes. At Hay River, Providence, Simpson, Fort Smith, Fort Macpherson, Resolution and Aklavik are schools for the natives. At Fort Resolution there are 255 dwellings, and about $60,000 worth of live stock; the furs trapped in that region were worth one year $115,000. In this watershed are the great game reserves of Yellowknife, Slave River, Thelon and Wood Buffalo.

These conditions ensure the steady development of the Mackenzie regions.

THE NORTHWESTERN FURS

Practically the only industry in the Northwest Territories is that of hunting. The fur trade of Canada has greatly increased in recent years. In 1914 the Dominion exported raw furs to the value of $5,109,000. In 1926 the value of such shipments was $16,859,759. The sum credited to the Northwest Territories was $1,625,875, one tenth of the whole. Contiguous countries furnish a great number of pelts, and it is safe to say that one half the furs come from arctic or sub-arctic regions. About five per cent are raised on fur farms, principally the silver fox. It is interesting to know that the most productive animal is the muskrat, followed in the order named by the beaver, mink, red, white and silver foxes.

Recognizing the value of its wild life, Canada has enacted provisions for its conservation. Licenses are required for hunting or trade; some species are protected during certain seasons, and the killing of others is prohibited for a number of years. Game and other preserves have been established, with beneficial results.

A Minister of the Dominion has said of the

industry: "The total output has not declined, and Canada may still be described as the last great fur preserve of the world." Of the regions beyond the last outpost of settlement, he adds: "It is the function of the fur trade to turn this vast domain to perpetual economic use." Such action will make Polar Canada a land of continuing prosperity.

THE NORTHERN INHABITANTS

However rich a land may be in natural resources, it cannot prosper without population, especially of men who labor with their hands. The Indians of these polar regions are located in the Mackenzie valley, and have been described as to numbers and races. The principal hewers of wood and drawers of water are the Eskimos. By the census of 1924 they numbered 6,688, distributed as follows: Northwest Territories, 2,888; Baffin Island, 1,900; Labrador and Ungava, 1,900. Canada has been prompt to recognize the necessity of conserving the welfare of its primitive races, which the influence of modern trade and contact with the civilized visitors have seriously disturbed.

The very existence of the natives depends on the large game of the country, now in danger of extermination from high-power guns. To ensure in the future food and raiment for them, the Dominion has sought to save the game by setting aside large areas as reserves. Four of these reserves — the Peel River, Slave, Thelon and Yellowknife —

include 240,000 square miles of land and forest. Only natives are permitted to hunt in these grounds, and while so doing cannot use either a shotgun or automatic rifle. The government has also established two game sanctuaries, where hunting is prohibited. In Wood Park, area 17,300 square miles, are gathered about five thousand buffalo, who are steadily increasing in number. The sanctuary for the few remaining herds of musk oxen is between lakes Beverly and Clinton-Colden, in a region where scattered oxen find suitable pasturage, and which is rarely visited by hunters. The proposition advanced by Stefansson looking to the importation and domestication of both musk oxen and reindeer is under consideration by a commission.

The Department of Indian Affairs gives careful attention to the promotion of the mental, physical and spiritual welfare of the Eskimos. The desirability of education along technical lines is admitted, but it is impossible to undertake it generally, owing to the inaccessible regions occupied by the wandering families. However, the government aids the mission schools for Eskimos at Aklavik, Shingle Point and Herschel Island in the Mackenzie district, as also in the Baffin Island schools.

Medical service is largely given by the police, who have first-aid kits and other simple appliances. The unusual freedom of the Eskimos from ordinary disease is notable. Physicians are sent wherever demands are urgent. In the Mackenzie district, not only is there one at Fort Macpherson, but at Aklavik there has been established an Eskimo Ward in All Saints Hospital; and there is also a graduate nurse stationed there. The annual trips north by boat enable the attending doctor to visit many settlements and render needful service.

In recent years the natives of the Coronation Gulf district have suffered greatly owing to the deflection from their old routes of the migrating caribou, on which they depended for food and clothing. The government has met the situation by sending into the district skilled fishermen, with ample materials in the way of nets, harpoons and other apparatus. It is hoped that under training the local Eskimos will catch sufficient fish, of which there are ample schools, to feed them in summer, and dry and store enough for winter. Quantities of food for relief in case of famine are also stored under the police control at convenient points, for issue when absolutely needed. It is believed that successful fishing operations will gradually overcome the recurrence of famines.

It is officially reported that the practice of infanticide is gradually dying out, though cases are still reported. The almost insupportable burden borne by the Eskimo mother at many times is appreciated. With the view to correcting the habit, the government has made arrangements for an Infant's Refuge near the Coronation Gulf, to be maintained under the Canadian police. Under existing plans such infants as are brought to the post will be cared for by Eskimo women until the children are old enough to return to their parents. Suitable food and simple medicines for the infants are provided (Jenness: "Report of Canadian Arctic Expedition." 1913–1918. Vols. xii–xv. Also Rasmussen: "Across Arctic America." 1927).

The prosperous condition of the Eskimos seems the least in the Hudson Bay region, but with interruptions improves westward to the Alaskan boundary. The largest settlement of Eskimos is at Aklavik in the Mackenzie delta. This village has a school, a hospital, three trading stations, a post-office and radio station. The Eskimos have about thirty small schooners, fitted with auxiliary power, with which they hunt and fish. When the season is over, they congregate at the village, sometimes to the number of several hundred. Trade is then brisk, and the comfortable houses are fitted with things brought from the far south. Among these are sewing machines, cameras, kerosene lamps, typewriters, safety razors and many ornaments for house and for dress. In this manner custom and fashion have invaded the coasts of the Arctic Ocean.

CHAPTER VII

CANADIAN ARCTIC ARCHIPELAGO

THE areas of the arctic islands of Canada approximate a million square miles, nearly twice that of all other northern islands. In 1880 the British Government ceded to the Dominion all claims to English territory in polar waters to the north of the continent of North America. The limits fixed were between longitudes 60° and 140° W. and northward to the Pole. Canada has not confined itself to a theoretical sovereignty but has substantiated its claims by occupation and administration.[1]

EXPLORATIONS

The basis of geographic knowledge of the principal islands south of the 75th parallel was laid by the voyage of William Parry, 1819–1820, in search of the Northwest Passage. Discovering Lancaster Sound, he sailed west through Barrow Strait and Melville Sound into M'Clure Strait, where he was turned back by impassable ice in 114° W., almost in sight of Beaufort Sea. Parry's most important discoveries to the north were the

[1] The northernmost islands are treated in Chapter VIII.

islands of North Devon, Cornwallis, Bathurst and Melville; at the latter he wintered. To the south were the islands of Cockburn, Somerset, Prince of Wales, Victoria and Banks (Parry: "Voyage for a Northwest Passage." 1821). His two voyages later added details only.

John Ross, 1829–1833, filled in unknown coasts east of Boothia — the most northerly land of the American continent — which he discovered (Ross: "Voyage for a Northwest Passage." 1835). By far the most important work done in this cruise of five years, which ended in the abandonment of the *Victory*, was the physical researches of James C. Ross. He not only explored the coasts of Boothia and King William Land, but acquired imperishable renown by locating the north magnetic pole at Cape Adelaide, in latitude 70° 5′ N., longitude 96° 46′ W. Amundsen, it may be added, during his northwest passage in 1903–1905, relocated it in 70° 30′ N., 95° 30′ W., a slight change in seventy years.

In Chapter III are noted the discoveries of Ross and of the Franklin Search expeditions. Though quite a number of arctic islands were located, they were of minor material value.

The explorations of the Canadian arctic archipelago by Vilhjalmur Stefansson, commander of the Canadian Arctic Expedition, 1913–1918, have been the most important since the voyages of Parry and Ross. Previous research work in the Canadian

[71]

Arctic (1906–1907 and 1908–1912) fitted Stefansson admirably for acquiring such information as would add to the prestige of the Dominion. Covering practically the entire archipelago, land and sea, his expeditions have contributed important knowledge in all branches of science — Anderson being in charge of natural history branches — relative to the regions north of Canada and Alaska.

Geographically his surveys are estimated to have withdrawn nearly 100,000 square miles from the areas of unknown seas and lands. Approximately these surveys cover 65,000 square miles of Beaufort Sea; 10,000 of the Arctic Ocean west of Prince Patrick Island, and nearly 20,000 to the east and northeast of Prince Patrick. In addition to verifying previous discoveries, and filling in unknown coast lines, original discoveries were made by him between latitudes 73° and 80.2° N., and longitudes 98° and 115° W.; these include three large and several small islands. His surveys define with considerable certainty the continental shelf of the Arctic Ocean to the north and west of the archipelago, and leave no unknown lands in this area. Remarkable was his journey on the moving floes of Beaufort Sea — living largely on seals — where a sounding of 2,561 fathoms marked the site of Keenan Land; other soundings disclosed a shelf of about 500 metres for 100 miles northwest of Ellef Ringness Islands. Remarkable were the experiences of his assistant Storkensen, who, with four companions, drifted 400 miles on moving floes, and made soundings and observations of special importance (Stefansson: "The Friendly Arctic." 1921. "Hunters of the Great North." 1922).

The official reports of the Stefansson expedition have been edited by R. M. Anderson, who commanded the southern party. They are the most valuable scientific contributions relative to Polar Canada ever published ("Report of the Canadian Arctic Expedition. 1913–1918." 16 vols.).

NATIVES

Apart from traders and officials the population are Eskimos; their number and distribution are indefinite. Probably they do not number more than 2,500. Those who may be classed as permanent are, in the main, on the islands of Baffin, Devon, Somerset, Victoria and Herschel. The northernmost village is Ponds Inlet, Baffin Land, though at Dundas harbor, Devon, 74° 30′ N., 82° 15′ W., there are temporary camps. To the west and north there are ruins of a former settlement, extending in Ellesmere Land to the Lake Hazen region, discovered by Greely in 1882.

The activities of the traders have resulted in the congregation of the natives in two regions: to the east on and adjoining Baffin Land, to the west between Victoria and Herschel islands. Intermediate are a few nomadic tribes, among which Rasmussen records 259 Eskimos in the Pelly Bay region. Wherever native activity promises industrial benefits the trading post appears.

Prominent in this respect are conditions in Baffin Land, one of the great islands of the world with its area of 211,000 square miles. Of its fifteen trading posts, the most important are Pangnirtung, Cumberland Sound, 66° N., and Ponds Inlet, about 72° 30′ N.; at each of these stations are a post-office, detachment of the Royal Canadian Police, and two trading posts. To the west, on Victoria Island — notable through Stefansson's Blond Eskimos — there are two trading establishments at Cambridge Bay, while the Eskimos of the adjacent regions are within easy reach of Bernard Harbor and six other posts ("Map of the Northwest Territories." 1926. Department of the Interior, Canada).

From its easy accessibility, abundant game and considerable population — estimated at a thousand — Baffin Land is the best known of the arctic islands, although its west coast between Cape Willoughby and Cape Konig is indefinitely charted, owing to the heavy ice of Fox Basin. However, much is known of the island in general, through the explorations of Hantzsch, 1910–1911; of Burwash, 1923–1924; of Soper, 1924–1926; and Wight. Their contributions covered ethnology, geography, geology, fauna and flora. Their reports are confirmed by casual visits of MacMillan and Putnam.

Conditions in the islands of Banks and Victoria, area 14,000 square miles, have been thoroughly described by the explorations and researches made by Stefansson and other members of the Canadian Arctic Expedition, 1913–1918. In *Reports*, vols. xii–xv, Jenness describes: "The Copper Eskimo", "Eskimo Folklore", "Eskimo Songs" and "Eskimo Language and Technology."

The Dominion of Canada gives much thought and expense to safeguard the welfare of the Eskimos in these remote isles. It has set aside the large preserve of Banks Island, Victoria Island and Arctic Island, where the Eskimos enjoy exclusively rights of hunting and trapping. The administrative duties are performed by an efficient force, the Royal Canadian Mounted Police, of which thirty-four are stationed in Yukon Territory, fifty-six in Northwest Territories, and thirteen on the remote arctic islands. The most northerly posts are Ponds Inlet, 72° 30' N., Dundas Harbor, 74° 30' and Bache Peninsula, 76° 04'. These stations are annually visited by ship, on which voyages are carried doctors, inspectors and at times justices (detailed from the Canadian courts), to take such action as may contribute to health, justice and order. These visits have brought about slowly improving conditions as to cleanliness, habitations, sanitation, health and previsionary economy.

The police maintain peace, relieve distress and administer the law. Among their varied duties are service as postmasters, coroners, custom officers, game wardens and fish inspectors. Duty at posts is supplemented by service in the field. To visit and aid remote encampments, no journey is too long, no cold too severe. No pains are spared to relieve distress, to ascertain resources, to enforce law.

Policeman Joy sledged one thousand and three hundred miles from Bache Peninsula westward to King Christian Island — duplicating the trip of MacMillan — to locate game and discover possible nomads.

To prevent possible famine, caused by deflection of route by migrating caribou, Eskimos of Baffin Land and the region around King William Land have been supplied with nets and other fishing gear for obtaining food. Besides introducing a new occupation, the authorities foster practical education. It extends assistance for the maintenance of the Eskimo Mission schools at Lake Harbour and Cumberland Gulf, Baffin Land. The remote arctic islands are practically without medical attention, but efforts are being made to alleviate the situation. It is planned to station a permanent doctor at Pangnirtung, Baffin Land, who will do much patrol work. Doctor Livingston, 1926–1927, traveled two thousand and five hundred miles to render aid and give advice to

[76]

the Eskimos. In this patrol, with Eskimo companions only, he visited every native settlement in Baffin Land. Such is the generous service rendered by Canada to its primitive folk, the Children of the Ice.

CHAPTER VIII

KANE SEA AND THE GREAT FROZEN OCEAN

Although these regions are not contributing to the world in any material way, daring souls have therein sought nature's hidden secrets, discovered unknown lands, and thus stimulated other adventurous spirits.

The sea bears the name of the first explorer who entered its waters, Elisha Kent Kane.   In a search for Franklin he pushed the *Advance* into its ice-encumbered area, to her final mooring place in Rensselaer Harbor, 78° 37′ N., 71° W.   The sledge parties of the expedition reached Cape Constitution on the Greenland coast, 80° 35′ N., whence ice-free Kennedy Channel was visible; and on the shore of Ellesmere Land Cape Frazier was attained.   With the *Advance* icebound, supplies exhausted, and casualties occurring, Kane abandoned his ship and succeeded in reaching Upernivik by boat (Kane: "Second Grinnell Expedition, 1853–1855." 2 vols. 1856. Kane's Observations in the Arctic Seas.   Vol. XI. Smithsonian Contributions to Knowledge).   Most interesting were their relations with the Eskimos

Courtesy of the Government of Norway

NORWEGIAN METEOROLOGICAL AND RADIO STATION ON JAN MAYEN ISLAND, GREENLAND SEA. AUSTRIAN-HUNGARIAN INTERNATIONAL POLAR STATION, 1882–83.

Department of the Interior, Canada

ROYAL CANADIAN POLICE STATION, 1924. POST DUNDAS, NORTH DEVON.

between Cape York and Etah, the most northerly inhabitants of the world.

The expedition of Hayes, 1860–1861, wintered in Foulke Fiord, near but south of Kane Sea. In the spring Hayes charted the shores of Ellesmere Land, between latitudes 77° and 78°, and added to arctic maps Hayes Sound and Bache Peninsula. Then sledging north he attained on that coast an indefinite point, on the shore of his "Open Polar Sea", which by astronomical observations he placed in 81° 35′ N., 70° 30′ W. Later surveys have accurately charted this region, and his observations are in error, — either a degree and a half of latitude, or six and a half of longitude. His farthest north has been considered to be Cape Joseph Goode, 80° 11′ N., the point which most closely agrees with his map, journal and narrative. This cape is at the southern end of Kennedy Channel, which for the greater part of the year is largely ice-free, due to the action of strong currents and high tides, which in the neaps reach a range of thirty feet. The scientific observations of the expedition were valuable contributions to arctic knowledge (Hayes: "Open Polar Sea." 1867. Hayes' Physical Observations. Vol. XV. Smithsonian Contributions to Knowledge).

The most extended and important discoveries in these regions were those made by Charles Francis Hall, 1870–1873. The *Polaris* was navigated to 82° 11′ N., in the Arctic Ocean, a northing never before attained by ship. She found refuge for the winter in Thank God Harbor, 81° 37′ N., 62° W. The harbor was unique, being an open roadstead on the coast of Greenland, where the ship was sheltered by an enormous floeberg, whose dimensions were 650 feet, by 400 by 300. Not only was the northing of Kane surpassed by four hundred miles, but Hall extended Grant Land and Greenland nearly two degrees of latitude towards the Pole, — the former practically to its northern limits. In reaching the most northern land ever attained by civilized man, he found that the ice cap of Greenland there ended, — and he was in an ice-free, vegetation-covered, game-frequented area of several thousand square miles. Hall died of disease that autumn, and all extended exploration ended.

The attempt to bring the *Polaris* back to the United States ended in shipwreck. Pushed into an impassable ice pack, she was anchored to a large floe. For two months she drifted southward slowly, and was off Northumberland Island when a violent gale disrupted the pack and nearly destroyed her. Terror-stricken, part of the crew escaped in the winter darkness to the floes, and the ship moving away, they were subjected to the horrors of a midwinter ice drift, during which they suffered extreme privations and experienced appalling dangers. After a drift of 1,300 miles in five months, the despairing party were rescued by the

Tigress, off Labrador, April 30, 1873, not only un-
reduced in numbers, but with the addition of a
girl baby born to Eskimo Hannah.

The party on the *Polaris* fared better. The
ship drifted to land, near Life-boat Cove, where
she was beached. From her remains Polaris House
was built, and boats were constructed in the succeeding spring. Starting for Upernivik, they met
the whaler *Ravenscraig*, on June 22, 1873 (Davis:
"Polaris Northpolar Expedition." 1876. Also,
Blake: "Arctic Experiences"; "Tyson's Drift."
1874).

The British Arctic Expedition of 1875–1876 is
usually known by the name of its commander,
George S. Nares. His squadron consisted of the
Alert and *Discovery*, which made the voyage from
Smith Sound under extremely adverse conditions
of ice and storm. Eventually the *Discovery* established her winter quarters in the land-locked
harbor of Lady Franklin Bay. The *Alert*, under
Nares, succeeded in entering the Arctic Ocean,
and wintered on the open coast, at Floeberg Beach,
82° 25′ N., 62° W.

Field work began at once and was continued
till late autumn. It was renewed in early spring,
and was fruitful of results. The most important
journey from the *Alert* was made by Markham,
who reached on the ice of the frozen sea 83° 20′ N.,
64° W., the highest north attained to that time.
Aldrich, who traced the arctic coast westward to

82° 16′ N., 86° W., where Grant Land trended to the southwest, not only discovered 220 miles of new land, but surpassed in his journey the record of northing made by Parry in 1827.

From the *Discovery* Archer explored the fiord named for him. Beaumont, crossing Robeson Channel to the Greenland coast, extended Hall's discoveries from Cape Bryant to the eastern shore of Sherard Osborne Fiord, in 82° 20′ N., 51° W. The discoveries of the expedition were made, however, at the expense of lives and limbs. The sledge parties were attacked by scurvy from which disease no less than thirty-six suffered on the *Alert*. Nares wisely returned the next summer to England (Nares: "Voyage to the Polar Sea." 2 vols. 1877. Also Markham: "Great Frozen Sea." 1878).

The geographic work done by the Nares expedition was extensive and important. It did not consist alone in carrying a British ship and in planting the Union Jack in a higher latitude on land and on sea than had ever been before attained. The coasts of Grant Land were surveyed from the head of Archer Fiord northward to Cape Columbia, and thence westward to its limit. The north shores of Greenland were extended from Cape Bryant to Cape Britannia, and Beaumont's observations disclosed that the land to the eastward of Sherard Osborne Fiord was equally ice-free as that discovered by Hall. The tidal, magnetic and meteorological observations were valuable contributions to these branches of physical science, and the unfailing courage and persistent energy of its officers and men added new laurels to the British navy.

Americans next entered the dangerous waters of Kane Sea, engaged neither in an attempt to navigate the "Open Polar Sea" nor to attain the Pole. The national Lady Franklin Bay expedition, under A. W. Greely, organized for systematic scientific work, occupied one of the fifteen International circumpolar stations; its special researches and its fortunes are set forth in Chapter XX. The scope and extent of its purely geographic contributions are here briefly summarized. Greely discovered and explored the interior of Grant Land, which proved to be an ice-free, lake-watered, vegetation-covered and game-frequented area of about 2,000 square miles, lying between two ice caps, — to the north and the south. From the summit of its loftiest peak, Mount C. A. Arthur, Greely noted the frozen sea to the west of the Garfield range. To the southwest through Greely Fiord was visible high land, doubtless the cliffs of Heiberg Land. Lockwood later crossed Grant Land from the head of Archer Fiord and skirting the southern ice cliffs reached in Greely Fiord the tidal waters of the western ocean. The journey which won the record of the farthest north is recorded in Chapter IX. It is to be noted that

the extended winter journeys made by Greely's
parties were entirely free from the casualties of
disease and violence, of life and limb which marked
in one phase or another the explorations in the
high north of Nares, Peary, Rasmussen, Sverdrup
and MacMillan (Greely: Three Years of Arctic
Service." 2 vols. 1886).

The many expeditions of Robert E. Peary,
1891–1909, were for the attainment of the North
Pole (Chapter XIX). However, his many explorations in this region had subsidiary results
of importance, since they not only confirmed the
successes of his predecessors, but also made contributions of value. In 1898, he determined the
peninsularity of Bache, considered by Hayes to
be an island. He also confirmed the forecast of
Greely, based on the discovery of Schley Land
closing Hayes Sound, that Ellesmere and Grant
formed one land, extending from Jones Sound to
Cape Columbia. Peary visited Heiberg Land and
filled in portions of the coasts not explored by
Sverdrup. He also charted the west coast of
Grant Land, discovered by Greely but not visited
in 1882, between Aldrich's farthest point and
Greely Fiord. Peary believed that in this last-
mentioned journey he had discovered a new land,
Crocker Land, which he charted in 83.5° N., 102°
W.; unfortunately MacMillan has proved its
nonexistence.

Most remarkable were his two journeys across

the great inland ice of Northern Greenland. In 1892 he sledged from Inglefield Gulf over ice of an elevation of eight thousand feet, to Navy Cliff, 81° 37' N., 34° E. Failing in his attempt in 1894, Peary succeeded in again crossing the ice cap, though adding nothing to his first discoveries. His judgment as to the geographic results were erroneous. He incorrectly held the same opinion as Greely, that the regions to the north of Navy Cliff formed a new land, when in fact it is part of Greenland. His reports as to the existence of a strait, and as to the nearness of Navy Cliff to the Greenland Sea have been proved unfounded through later accurate surveys by Mylius-Erichsen, Mikkelsen and Rasmussen ("Meddelelser om Gronlund", vol. 44 ; and Rasmussen : "Greenland by the Polar Sea." Also Peary : "Northward over the Great Ice"). In 1900 Peary rounded Greenland in 83° 39', nine miles farther north than Lockwood's discoveries of 1882, and traced the eastern shores to 83° N., 25° W. ; however, this did not complete Greenland's coast lines, as claimed by him. Despite fallacious claims, Peary's contributions to the geography of these regions are unsurpassed by those of any other explorer, except Hall, in extent and variety.

The two journeys of Rasmussen from Thule, on North Star Bay, to extreme northern Greenland made final contributions to geographic knowledge. The first expedition, in 1912, crossed the inland ice from Inglefield Gulf to Denmark Fiord, where extensive surveys were made. By charting, Rasmussen established that the channel which Peary thought he had discovered was nonexistent. Rasmussen's expedition of 1917, with botanist Wulff and geologist Koch, followed the coast from North Star Bay to De Long Fiord (of Lockwood, 1882). Rasmussen surveyed the inlets and fiords between St. George Fiord and De Long Fiord, giving special attention to the ramifications of the last-named waterway. The lateness of the season obliged him to make the return journey across the inland ice from St. George Fiord to Humboldt Glacier. Game failed and disasters occurred, causing the death of Wulff and the Eskimo Harrigan. The scientific results of the expedition were important. Wulff's researches were devoted to biology, especially to discovering the methods of life and reproduction of plants and animals under the harsh condition of existence in high arctic regions. His notes form the basis of Ostenfeld's memoir, "Fauna and Flora on the North Coast of Greenland", an appendix in Rasmussen's "Greenland." Another appendix of special value is that of L. Koch, "Geological Observation on Northwestern Greenland."

The most daring and dangerous journeys from the Kane Sea base have been the crossing of the inland ice to the northeastern coast of Greenland. In 1892 Peary initiated this perilous traverse.

Eskimo Tupek at Bache Peninsula, 1926. The Northernmost
Encampment of the World.

Crossing the divide between Kane Sea and Whale Sound, Peary reached the inland ice May 24, with sixteen dogs and four sledges. The supporting division under Cook was sent back, and with Astrup and two teams Peary marched onward. Traveling via Petermann and St. George Fiords, they reached on July 4 Navy Cliff — elevation 4,000 feet — in 81° 37′ N., 34° W. To the north they saw an ice-free land, dominated by snowy peaks, such as Lockwood found farther north. To the east was an ice-covered inlet, erroneously thought by Peary to be the Greenland Sea. To-day it is known to be more than a hundred miles farther to the eastward, as determined by the surveys of three expeditions, — Mylius-Erichsen, Mikkelsen and Rasmussen (Peary: "Northward over the Great Ice"). In the return journey to McCormick Bay, 450 miles distant, the ice crest was crossed in about 8,000 feet.

Peary renewed his efforts in 1893, with eight men, twelve sledges and ninety-two dogs. Storm-bound by a violent blizzard on March 14, after marching one hundred and thirty-four miles, he saw his Eskimos frost-bitten and his dogs dying. Sending back his disabled men, with indomitable but fruitless energy he proceeded with three selected men. In fourteen days they made only eighty-five miles, and conditions became desperate; his men broke down and more dogs died. Retreat was inevitable, and safety was doubtful. Abandoning all equipment and sledges, they reached Bowdoin Bay April 15, with only twenty-six dogs living of the original ninety-two.

His last journey, in 1895, displayed the same courage but was equally fruitless in its final results. With Lee and Henson, four Eskimos, six sledges and sixty-three dogs, Peary started on April 2. Traveling was so bad that on the third march an Eskimo deserted with his team. Deep snow and bad weather, together with his inability to find pemmican previously cached obliged Peary to divide his party when one hundred and thirty-four miles inland. All the Eskimos were sent back, and with the utmost rashness he pushed northward with Lee and Henson, their three sledges being drawn by forty-one dogs. Lee became disabled by frostbite, the ill-fed dogs began to die and food for the men was nearly gone ; soon it was evident that they would perish unless game was found. About May 15 they reached Independence Fiord in desperate straits, one man disabled, their single sled broken and only eleven exhausted dogs remaining. Fortunately, they discovered a herd of eleven musk oxen, which temporarily relieved their distress. However, no other game was found, and two more dogs died ; it was doubtful if any one could escape death when they began a frantic race homeward to escape starvation. Abandoning everything except food, twenty-five forced marches brought them utterly exhausted to Bowdoin Bay on June 25.

If Peary's advance beyond his buried cache was one of the rashest of arctic journeys, yet the courage and physical endurance displayed by him and his companions place their efforts among notable feats in polar sledging. However, it emphasized the rule that a reserve party is a necessary adjunct to successful arctic exploration.

In 1896 and 1897, Peary obtained and brought to the United States several meteorites from the vicinity of Cape York. Among these is the largest known meteorite of the world, weighing nearly one hundred tons.

In 1900 he made his last journey to northern Greenland, which he rounded in 83° 39′ N., nine miles farther north than Lockwood's discoveries of 1882. While Peary traced the northeast coast of Greenland, he did not complete the coast lines of Greenland.

The final charting of the west shores of Ellesmere Land was done by the expedition of Sverdrup, 1899–1902. Failing in his attempt to circumnavigate Greenland, in 1900 he transferred his explorations to the unknown regions northwest of Jones Sound. He discovered the continuity of Ellesmere Land from Jones Sound to the north cape of Hansen Sound, 81° 37′ N., 92° W., about sixty miles southwest of Cape Alfred Ernest, of Aldrich, 1876. The west coast has many bays and inlets, of which the largest are Greely Fiord and Bauman Fiord. For some unexplained reason he renamed Schley

Land (Greely, 1884) at the head of Buchanan Bay with Norwegian titles. To the west of Ellesmere Land he discovered, and explored in part, about a dozen islands, of which the largest is Heiberg Island. This archipelago extends north to 80° 37′, and west to longitude 102°. His explorations confirmed the opinion of Greely, who first discovered the west coast north of Greely Fiord, as to the limited westerly extent of Ellesmere Land.

Sverdrup's discoveries as a whole were most important. They doubtless complete the southern littoral boundary of the main north polar basin, filling in as they do to the north of the Parry Islands the gap between Finlay Island, 1853, and Greely Fiord, 1883. The geological collections of Schei were extensive and illuminating: Cambrian, Silurian and Devonian formations in south Ellesmere Land; Mesozoic formations and Tertiary deposits on Heiberg Island and the shores of Greely Fiord. Unfortunately the meteorological observations were not supplemented by magnetic work (Sverdrup: "Four Years in the Arctic Regions." 2 vols. 1904).

From 1913–1917, Donald MacMillan, from his base at Etah, made very extensive explorations of Ellesmere Island and adjacent regions, both on land and at sea, to the west and north. In his sledge trips he covered eight thousand miles in which he supplemented and extended the work of his predecessors. The interior of Grant Land, the Sverdrup Islands and the Parry Archipelago were the most interesting fields of his operations. In his sledging trips he discovered nine unknown islands.

Most important was his journey over the Great Frozen Sea, in which he eliminated the mythical Crocker Land of Peary. This trip, from February 7 to March 24, 1914, was made by crossing Ellesmere Land, up Eureka Strait to the North Cape of Heiberg Land, where his men faced the ice-clad ocean. They had marched 580 miles in 33 days, and success seemed certain. Unfortunately, from the high cliffs no land was to be seen. However, over the sea floes they marched to the northwest, for the land reported to be 120 miles distant. On March 24 they were in latitude 82° 30′ N., longitude 103° 32′ W., 150 miles northwest from Heiberg Land, and thirty miles beyond the allotted land. The weather was clear but no land was in sight. The declination of the compass was 178 degrees west, and the ocean was very deep. During this journey Green killed an Eskimo, fearing desertion and abandonment. Conditions were similar to those under which an Eskimo had killed Marvin, of Peary's party.

In 1916 MacMillan made a long sledge trip to King Christian Land, never before visited, and believed to be Finlay Island of Osborn, 1853. This ended his field explorations (MacMillan: "Four Years in the White North." Revised edition, 1925). His later trip is recorded under "Arctic Aviation", Chapter XVIII.

Canada has occupied Ellesmere Land by establishing police stations, that on Bache Peninsula being the most northerly.

CHAPTER IX

GREENLAND

VIEWING Australia as a continent, Greenland is the largest island in the world, having an area of 830,000 square miles, of which less than ten per cent. is habitable. While Cape Farewell is seven degrees south of the arctic circle, Cape Jesup is within six degrees of the North Pole. In its widest part capes Alexander and Bismarck are separated by nine hundred miles.

Greenland is an elevated plateau as a whole, ranging from two thousand to nine thousand feet above the ocean. Its precipitous, rocky coasts are broken by numerous intersecting fiords, former beds of the extensive glaciers, which debouch from the inland ice. The permanent ice sheet covers nine tenths of the country, and attains an unknown thickness, possibly three thousand feet.

DISCOVERY AND EXPLORATIONS

Discovered by Erik the Red in the tenth century, the southwestern coasts were explored and settled by the Norsemen in succeeding years. It was the first European settlement in the western world. Extensive research by Danish scientists has

[93]

revealed the story of its fate. Gradually the colony died out, probably in the fourteenth century, — its men, women and children deteriorating physically, as shown by physiological studies of the remains. In its best days it built a cathedral, houses, barns, etc., and maintained considerable herds of animals. By keeping up its relations with Europe, its members were Christianized and literate (Norlund *et al.* Buried Norsemen at Herjolfsen. Med. on Greenland. V. lxvii).

The western shores of Greenland were rediscovered in the sixteenth century (See Chapter I), and the eastern coasts by whalers, Lambert (1670) reaching 78° N. Among Danish explorers were Dannell (1652) to 65° N., and Walloe, from the west coast to 61° N. (1752) on the east shore.

The opening of the nineteenth century was marked by geographic ignorance as to Greenland. In the map of Barrow, 1818, the great British arctic authority, Baffin Bay was omitted. Barrington the same year was more explicit, for he entered on his map the legend "Baffin Bay, according to the relation of W. Baffin in 1616, but not now believed." Later northern extensions of the west shores of Greenland were made by Inglefield, 1852, 78° 28' N., 74° W.; Kane, 1854, Cape Constitution, 80° 10' N.; Hall, 1871, 82° 07' N., 59° W.; Greely, 1882, Cape Washington, 83° 30' N.; Peary, 1900, Cape Jesup, the northernmost point of Greenland, 83° 39′ N. These northings are further described in Chapter VIII.

The first important discoveries in East Greenland were those made in 1822 by the famous Scotch whaler, Captain William Scoresby, Jr., who, sailing with his father, had seen the coast in 1817 and in 1821. The elder Scoresby in the *Fame* explored Scoresby Sound and other adjacent inlets; he erred in thinking that the Sound bisected Greenland, as reported by Frobisher in 1576. The younger Scoresby was indefatigable in acquiring information regarding the land and the adjacent sea. In intervals of fishing he surveyed the coast with care and accuracy, by astronomical and trigonometric observations. In June, 1822, when in the *Baffin*, he sketched and charted the coast from Hold-with-Hope of Hudson, 1607, in 73° 30′ N., to Gale Hamke Bay, of Hamke, 1654, in 75° N. He found the coast barren, rugged and precipitous, with elevations ranging from one thousand to six thousand feet. His accumulated knowledge was set forth in his valuable volume, "Voyage to the Northern Whale Fishery."

Geographically Scoresby's discoveries were of far greater importance than those of any other in the Greenland Sea. It was not alone that he surveyed and charted with unusual accuracy a coast some eight hundred miles long by its windings, but he changed entirely the geographic features of East Greenland as then known.

On existing charts the east coast between the
69th and 75th parallels was laid down with a
southwest trend, covering 23 degrees of longitude,
from 5° to 28° W. Scoresby reduced the longitu-
dinal extent of East Greenland by nearly three
fourths, and determined the coast direction to be
nearly due south and north, between longitudes
19° and 25° W. His scientific work, done in the
intervals of successful fishing, was so abundant
and comprehensive that it may be safely said that
no other save Nordenskiold had contributed so
materially to a scientific knowledge of the arctic
regions. Clavering, in the *Griper*, skirted in 1823
the east coast from Cape Parry, 72.5° N. to Shan-
non Island, 75° 12′ N. Exploring Hamke Bay
he discovered an ice fiord with discharging glaciers,
and found its shores inhabited by Eskimos.
Meanwhile his subordinate, Sabine, made pendulum observations on Pendulum Islands, 74° 32′ N.

Koldewey, of the second German north-polar
expedition, wintered at Pendulum Island, 1869–
1870, whence extended explorations were made.
By sledge, latitude 77° 01′ N. was reached. The
regions in and near Fligely Fiord were explored
by land. When the *Germania* was released from
the ice, Koldewey discovered and entered Franz
Josef Fiord, which penetrates inland five degrees
of longitude, reaching 73° 11′ N., 25° 58′ W.
Payer describes the fiord as a combination of
"huge walls, deep erosion fissures, wild peaks,

[96]

mighty crevassed glaciers, raging torrents and
lofty waterfalls." One peak rose behind it over
five thousand feet, and adjacent Mount Petermann
was estimated to be nearly twelve thousand feet
high. The expedition contributed an important
series of scientific memoirs on arctic subjects
(Koldewey: "Second German North Polar Expedition." 1874).

Important as were the American, English and
German explorations, they made minor contributions as compared with researches made under the
Royal Greenland Commission in nearly a hundred
Danish expeditions. The Commission has presented in eighty or more finely illustrated volumes
the results obtained. These memoirs cover botany, ethnology, mineralogy, — indeed, all branches
of natural history; they are indispensable to every
student of Greenland. Space does not permit
bibliographic notes. However, important discoveries are set forth in these volumes: "Meddelelser
om Gronland." Holm and Garde, 1883–1885,
vols. 9, 10; G. Ryder, 1891–1892, vols. 17, 18,
19; Amdrup, 1898–1900, vols. 27, 28, 29, 30;
Mylius-Erichsen, 1906–1908, vols. 42, 43, 44, 45,
46; E. Mikkelsen, 1909–1912, vol. 53; Kruuse
(botanical), 1912, vol. 49.

The expedition of Mylius-Erichsen, in the
Danmark, disclosed all features of the northeastern coast hitherto unknown. His assistant, Koch,
reached 83.5° N., thus completing the outline of

Greenland, erroneously claimed by Peary. The most important discoveries were made by Mylius, with Bronlund and Hage. Remarkable conditions were found to exist south of Lambert Land. Along a stretch named Glacier Gulf, for a distance of one hundred and forty miles, the inland ice moves steadily into Greenland Sea; the only view from the sea towards the coast was an unbroken front of towering ice cliffs, hundreds of feet above the ocean.

North of Lambert Land, from the 80th parallel, the coast as charted by Peary ("Northward over the Great Ice") proved to be entirely erroneous. Where Peary charted the Greenland Sea immediately east of Navy Cliff, Mylius discovered and mapped the northeast coast of Amdrup Land, which extends eastward twenty degrees of longitude, halfway from Navy Cliff to Spitsbergen. Peary Channel is nonexistent, being replaced on the chart of Mylius by Independence Fiord, from which jut inland other fiords, both north and south.

Mylius and his comrades perished of starvation, but they left safely cached charts and records of their discoveries. The recovery of these records is due to the daring journeys of E. Mikkelsen, made from Scoresby Sound during his expedition of 1909–1912 ("Meddelelser om Gronland", vol. 52).

In 1926–1927 Koch discovered in the Scoresby

Courtesy Royal Danish Commission on Greenland

ESKIMO CONGREGATION AT UPERNIVIK, GREENLAND.

Department of the Interior, Canada

ESKIMO AT NORTH DEVON, ENTRANCE TO LANCASTER SOUND, 1925,
NORTHWEST PASSAGE.

Sound and adjacent region great numbers of fossils, representing three geological ages. Many palms and like plants indicate that Greenland once enjoyed a tropical climate.

THE INLAND ICE

Explorations have not been confined to the limited ice-free regions of Greenland, but have comprised an examination of one of the most wonderful areas of the arctic regions, the glacial covering of nine tenths of the island. This covering, known as the inland ice, was long pictured as intersected here and there by ice-free valleys, where reindeer pastured on luxuriant vegetation. This theory was based on the presence of several projecting, barren peaks; these projections, called *nunitaks* by the Eskimos, were fancied to indicate the dwelling places of *kivigtoks*, or sorcerers having supernatural powers.

Attempts to cross the inland ice failed wholly or in part by Pars, 1728; Dalager, 1751; Whymper, 1867; Nordenskiold, 1870 and 1883; Jensen, 1878; and Peary, 1886. Nansen, in 1888, was the first to cross Greenland. In his journey from Cape Dan, on the east coast, to Godthaab on the west coast, he found an unbroken expanse of ice, which rose to an altitude of 7,000 feet (Nansen: "First Crossing of Greenland." 1886). Leaving the east coast, De Quervain crossed from Angmagsalik, on the arctic circle, to Jacobshavn

[99]

Fiord. The glacial covering where traversed reached a height above 9,500 feet, while a distant peak was estimated to have an elevation of 12,000 feet ("Meddelelser om Gronland", vol. 59). The longest traverse across the inland ice, was that made with ponies by J. P. Koch, in 1913. In this notable journey from Danmark Harbor, on the east coast, to Upernivik on the west, he passed over higher ice than his predecessors, 9,800 feet. The area of highest elevation is supposed to be in about 75° N. Remarkable were the crossings made northeasterly from the west coast, those of Peary, 1892 and 1894, and of Rasmussen, 1912 and 1917, noted in Chapter VIII. The inland ice, covering an area of about eight hundred thousand square miles, flows steadily into the ocean through the fiords, its rate of motion varying largely according to locality. While the thickness of the ice cap cannot be determined, it is evident that in places it reaches several hundred feet.

POPULATION AND GOVERNMENT

Since the extinction of the Norse colonists in the fifteenth century, the population of Greenland has been exclusively Eskimo, save the few score whites, — officials and missionaries. The efforts of Egede, 1721–1731, to colonize the west coast failed, but it led to the religious training of the natives.

It is the impression of many, slightly modified by recent visiting expeditions, that the Eskimos of Greenland are a primitive, ignorant, unchristianized race, — unprogressive and decadent through casual contact with a superior civilization. Snow huts in winter, rock igloos in summer for shelter, and seal oil a luxurious food, are fanciful pictures often presented.

As a matter of fact they are Christians, live comfortably, are literate and to a certain extent artistic. They are a peaceful, law-abiding, self-supporting people. They hold fast to their racial heritage, retain their language, and at the larger settlements have, during the past century, had a literature, expressed in Eskimo text in pertinently illustrated books and pamphlets. Every settlement from Cape Farewell north to Upernivik, about a thousand miles, presents evidence of the fostering care of Denmark for their mental and spiritual welfare, in the shape of churches and schools. For these purposes Denmark has spent more than $95,000 during 1927. These educative facilities are highly valued by the natives, who as a community or nation stand high in literacy. Detailed accounts of life methods are to be found in Rink: "The Eskimo Tribes" ("Meddelelser om Gronland", vol. xi); Rasmussen: "The People of the Polar North." 1908; Rasmussen: "Greenland by the Polar Sea." 1921.

The population of Greenland numbers about 16,000, of whom some 750 are on the east coast and 250 north of Cape York. The main body of

15,000 occupy the west coast from Cape Farewell north a thousand miles to the Upernivik district. The increases have been unbroken the past century. While there were 10,207 in 1892, the census of 1921 aggregated 14,355, of whom only 274 were whites.

Denmark by wise action has conserved the perpetuation of this primitive folk, by debarring foreign ships from its ports, and by establishing a trade monopoly, which, under governmental supervision, ensures fair returns for native products. The control rests in the Royal Greenland Bureau of the Department of the Interior. The Director of Greenland resides in Copenhagen, while there are two inspectors — one for North Greenland, at Godhavn, and one for South Greenland at Godthaab — who supervise the local traders. They have magisterial powers, and are responsible to the Director. The Christian spirit of Denmark is strikingly exhibited by its continued efforts to promote the welfare of Greenland, at an expense of many thousand dollars annually, the deficit in the budget for which tends to increase steadily. The future is anything but promising, since frequent arctic expeditions have introduced so-called methods of civilized life, claiming that they raise the standard of native life. The rifle has caused the almost complete extermination of large land game, and the introduction of luxuries are injurious to Eskimo economy.

Courtesy of the Royal Danish Commission on Greenland

ANGMAGSSALIK, ESKIMO COLONY ESTABLISHED BY DENMARK ON THE EAST COAST OF GREENLAND.

Denmark has added to its expense by the care of the Etah Eskimos, striving to counteract the local demoralization caused by visiting expeditions. In this region the explorer Rasmussen has established at Thule, on Inglefield Gulf, a trading station.

On the east coast there were formerly Eskimo settlements as far north as the 74th parallel, which have been largely deserted, through famine or disease. Denmark assumed the care of the remnant in 1910 by establishing a relief station at Angmagsalik, 65° 37′ N., debarring foreign exploitation. Norway claimed long-established rights of hunting, etc., on the coast. Prolonged discussion ended in the treaty of July 9, 1924, under which Norway retains certain rights from Lindenow Fiord, 60° 27′ N., to the 81st parallel, excepting the limits of the Danish Angmagsalik district. England is granted the same privileges. Norway in 1922 looked to permanent occupation by erecting a radio station at Mygbutken, 73° 30′ N., which is maintained during the fishing season, when weather reports are sent.

Denmark has increased the Eskimo populations by establishing the Amdrup station at Scoresby Sound, 70° 29′ N., 22° W. Danish officials care for the instruction and welfare of the Eskimos, and a visiting ship keeps them annually in direct connection with the world, as will the planned radio station with its weather reports from Angmagsalik.

[103]

The financial burden borne by Denmark in caring for Greenland is shown by the expenses for 1925–1926, of $943,000, as against receipts of $800,000. Of the receipts ninety per cent. are derived from the kryolite mine, the balance being in fish, skins and oils.

CHAPTER X

JAN MAYEN AND THE GREENLAND SEA

SEPARATED from other lands by oceanic depths far greater than the height of its famous Beeren-berg, isolated Jan Mayen Island in 70° N., 83° W., — fog-enshrouded and ice-beset — is the sole tiny bit of occupied land in the great Greenland Sea. Discovered by Hudson in 1607 and named Touches, it was claimed and occupied by the Dutch, to the discomfiture of England. Its whaling history is described later.

For nearly two centuries Jan Mayen was merely a geographic phrase, until in 1817 it was visited and surveyed by that scientific whaler, William Scoresby, Jr. He reported that Mount Esk was an active volcano, the most northerly in the world. It was visited in 1856 by Lord Dufferin, who described it charmingly in "Letters from High Latitudes." Rabot, landing on its unfrequented east coast in 1891, explored Esk and Faskrud fiords.

The most important phase in the history of Jan Mayen was its occupation in 1882 by the Austrian Von Wohlgemuth (Chapter XIX) for scientific research. In his report, Wien, 1886, appeared a general description, excellent maps, and scientific memoirs on the glaciers and other physical subjects. The ubiquitous arctic fox and an occasional polar bear were present.

In recent years there have been occasional visits by Norwegian hunters, and in 1920 there was installed by the Norwegian Geophysical Institute a wireless station, which yet remains. Its personnel consists of three men, who are relieved annually, owing to their isolated and arduous service. They daily report by radio to Norway the meteorological conditions, which render it possible to forecast the violent storms which coming from the northwest often prove destructive to shipping along the Norwegian coasts. It is one of the triumphs of science that Jan Mayen has been transformed into an arctic outpost to conserve the safety of mankind.

Thus in the twentieth as in the tenth century, Norway exercises its arctic activities in two hemispheres, from its North Cape westward to Greenland.

THE GREENLAND SEA

This sea is a southward extension of the arctic Ocean between Greenland and Spitsbergen. Varying in depth from 1,600 to 2,000 fathoms, it has an ice-covered area which in summer never decreases below 250,000 square miles, and at times exceeds 400,000 square miles. Fortunately for navigation, the sea is distinctly separated from the eastern half of the North Atlantic by a shallow submarine ridge, extending from the Faroes to Iceland. This barrier forces towards East Greenland the great ice fields, which, drifting south, often reach in part the banks of Newfoundland.

The Greenland Sea was the field of the most important industry of the arctic regions prior to the twentieth century, — the northern whale fishery. Its initiation was due to the voyage of Hudson, in 1607, when he discovered the vast number of whales and walrus which frequented these waters. The products of the Greenland whale fishery must have approximated two hundred million dollars, as Holland alone drew from this sea values of about ninety millions. This industry had two periods, — one of the coast, the other of the open sea (Conway: "No Man's Land." 1906).

COAST FISHING

In this phase the Dutch occupied in 1611 as their land base the island of Jan Mayen, the Hudson Touches of 1607. They built half a dozen cookeries principally on the northwest coast. The most important station was at North (English) Bay, where they had ten cookeries, equipped with boats, ovens, vats, etc. The efforts to establish a colony ended with the death of its seven mariners in 1634. This attempt at permanent settlement was caused

[107]

by the action of Biscayen whalers who visited and plundered the station in 1632, destroying what they could not carry away. One must remember that there were pirates in those days, called honest adventurers when they raided foreign stations for the benefit of their own nation.

The first boiling or reducing station was established by Mary Muss of Rotterdam at Muss Bay. The success of the Dutch whalers, as set forth by Zorgdrager, was such that in its best days Jan Mayen yielded so much train-oil that in one year two full extra cargoes of a thousand quartels each had to be fetched away in a special ship, which made two voyages for that purpose in one season.

Difficult ice navigation and the disappearance of whales from the coasts caused the Dutch to leave Jan Mayen about 1635, precipitously it would seem, from the amount of supplies and equipment there abandoned.

Meantime the Dutch pursued whaling along the coasts of Spitsbergen. England viewed with alarm this competition, and attempted enforcement of a monopoly on an ill-founded claim of initial discovery of the country. An English fleet seized the Dutch ships, but, worsted in an engagement with a Hollandish whale fleet in 1618, it agreed to a compromise, under which harbors were allotted equitably. The extreme north of Spitsbergen fell to Holland, while the southern ports were distributed to England, France, the Hanse towns, etc.

During the most profitable period of the Dutch fishery — 1620–1635 — it is stated that three hundred ships, with equipages of over fifteen thousand men, annually visited Spitsbergen ; Lamont says that more than eighteen thousand whalemen were on the coast in one summer. The industry required local reduction plants.

The most remarkable of these establishments was on Amsterdam Island, where on a broad plain grew up the astonishing village of Smeerenberg (Greasetown). Here, nearly within ten degrees of the North Pole, in 79° 50′ N., prevailed in summer conditions of comfort that would scarcely be credited by a visitor of to-day. Several hundred ships, with more than fifteen thousand men, anchored there annually. The population consisted not alone of the whalers and land-laborers, but of the camp followers, who always frequent centers of great and rapid productivity.

In the train of whalers followed merchant vessels, loaded with brandy, tobacco and toothsome edibles lacking in the plain fare of the hardy fishers. Shops were opened, drinking booths erected, while laborers and visiting whalemen were quartered in wooden, tile-covered houses. Even bakeries were constructed, and, as in Holland, the sound of the baker's horn drew crowds of eager purchasers for the fresh, hot bread. If reports err not, even the Dutch frau of 1630 was sufficiently enterprising to visit Smeerenberg (79° 50′ N.) and take away

[109]

the record of the farthest north from her Russian
sister of 1735, and her French rival, Madame
D'Aunet, of 1839 (79° 35' N.).

When shore fisheries failed, Smeerenberg fell
into decadence; demolished furnaces, unfilled
chaldron-frames, broken tools, dilapidated houses
of the one thousand and two hundred summer
residents were soon ruins, with only the polar
bears as spectators. The church was gone, the
fort dismantled, the large warehouses and cookeries, of which there were originally a score —
some two-storied and nearly a hundred feet long —
were sorry reminders of Dutch enterprise. Of the
few houses remaining in 1671, Martens says:
"They are built after this fashion . . . there is a
stove before with a ceiling at top, and behind a
chamber taking in the whole house. A kettle was
standing as it was set."

But human interest did not pass with the van-
ishing habitations of Smeerenberg, for on the
shores of that bay rest the last mortal remains
of more than a thousand stalwart fishers, who
ended their lives of toil and struggle in view of the
icy sea that had often witnessed their triumphs
over the leviathan of the deep. Storm-stayed
and ice-beset no longer, their dust awaits the
change and fate ordained by God's eternal laws.
In 1818, Holland erected a monument to the dead
on Amsterdam Island, where Buchan in that year
counted one thousand graves on the site.

Courtesy of the Minister of Iceland

HERRING CATCH FROM GREENLAND SEA BY ICELANDERS.

Courtesy of the Minister of Iceland

ICELANDIC FISHING FLEET.   STEAM TRAWLER IN FOREGROUND.

The aspect of this most northerly cemetery of the world finds its parallel in other harbors of Spitsbergen. That in Magdalena Bay, 79° 35′ N., is thus described by Madame D'Aunet, who visited it in the *Recherche*, 1839.

"I counted fifty-two graves in this cemetery, which is the most forbidding in the wide world; a cemetery without epitaphs, without monuments, without flowers, without remembrances, without tears, without regrets, without prayers; a cemetery of desolation, where oblivion doubly environs the dead, where is heard no sigh, no voice, no human step; a terrifying solitude, a profound and frigid silence, broken only by the fierce growl of the polar bear or the moaning of the storm."

The coast whaling of England failed to equal in success that of the Dutch. Commenced about 1612 as a monopoly under the Muscovy Company, it was marked by quarrels both at home and abroad (Conway: "No Man's Land", for details). Its land bases were principally in Bell, Horn and Ice sounds. They were abandoned as unprofitable when the whales kept to the open sea, avoiding the bays.

WHALING ON THE HIGH SEA

The shore fisheries failed about 1640, when recourse was had to the broad ocean. The Greenland Sea was thereafter the whaling resort of the various nations. Disasters and the wars sadly interfered with whaling, which became decadent to a certain degree about 1675. However, conditions improved greatly, and in 1697 the catch was unprecedented, 1,968 whales, whereof the value was $1,800,000. The Dutch sent forth 129 of the 201 ships, and shared to the extent of more than $1,200,000. The summer of 1701 was another great season, when 207 Dutch ships caught no less than 2,072 whales.

In the twentieth century the Greenland Sea has become a great sealing ocean where Norwegian mariners capture large numbers of the saddleback seal, which resort to the drifting ice packs as their breeding places. From these arctic waters — floe-covered, almost unnavigable, cloud-enshrouded — hardy Icelandic fishermen also garner benefits from the countless schools of the prolific cod and the humbler herring.

CHAPTER XI

ICELAND

IT appears desirable to include within the realm of polar regions the sovereign state of Iceland, as its northernmost points lie within the arctic zone. Inhabited for more than a thousand years, its recorded history sets forth the most notable tenacity of civilized man in surmounting adverse nature. On a volcanic-stricken, snow-enshrouded island these Norsemen upbuilt a nation distinguished for courage and resourcefulness, frugality and intelligence, temperance and peacefulness.

Its area of 40,000 square miles, the size of Ohio, has habitable ground of less than 10,000; the remaining three fourths are lava streams, snow fields and elevated deserts. One snow field, Vatna Jokull, covers 3,200 square miles, while other beds and 120 glaciers raise this arctic covering to 5,700 square miles. The outflow of 107 volcanoes remains in 4,700 square miles of lava streams.

THE EARLIER CENTURIES

Settled before the tenth century, Iceland was a free State for more than two centuries. Brought under the crown of Norway in 1261, it passed to

Denmark in 1280, being already Christianized. Iceland became an independent nation in 1918, under an Act of Union with Denmark. Its legislative body, the Althing, has existed for nearly a thousand years, modified and interrupted from time to time, — a maximum record for a democratic legislature.

At times through the centuries, Nature seemed determined to force the abandonment of this environment by arctic snows and torrid volcanoes. The overwhelming eruption of Laki, 1783, caused enormous destruction of houses, farm equipment and stock. The years following, epidemics and famine were marked by several thousand deaths. The most violent eruptions since were Hekla (eighteenth eruption), 1845; Katla, 1860; and Askja, 1875. The hardness of life and such disasters stimulated emigration, and a colony of about twenty thousand settled in Manitoba, Canada.

While much food was obtained from cattle and other animals imported from Norway, the lack of agricultural success obliged the Icelanders to depend almost entirely on the products of the Greenland Sea, — cod, herring, whales, walrus and seal, which are later described.

Although the Arctic Sea washes its coasts, the climate is mild, — warm winters and cool summers. The average winter temperatures along all the coasts are between 31° and 32°; on the interior uplands much colder. The summer averages range from 43° to 50° along the coast, higher in the interior.

CHANGES IN THE TWENTIETH CENTURY

The admission of Iceland into the family of nations in 1918 stimulated previous civic activities, and led to important changes in methods of life, conduct of trade, local intercourse and means of transportation. Isolation of families is now rare, and the individualistic spirit of former days has given way somewhat to community coördination. The critical and beneficial changes have been concessions won from Denmark: the abolition of the trade monopoly in 1854; the Icelandic Constitution of 1874; and especially the Home Rule of 1904. The King of Denmark is the nominal head of the government, who, with his Icelandic council, has limited powers. The Althing is the legislative assembly, which meets in Reykjavik. It consists of two houses, the upper of six members, appointed for eight years, while the lower house of thirty-six members is elected by the people, — women being voters. Having no army or navy, the foreign policy and defense are entrusted to Denmark. Regard for the incapacitated is shown by the old age pension. The nation subsidizes the Evangelical Lutheran Church, but there are no restrictions on other creeds.

Political independence has been followed by activity in trade, pride in accomplishment, in-

[115]

creased standards of living, which have discouraged emigration.

CULTURAL CONDITIONS

The former means of education have been improved through new institutions. In the national university four additional faculties have been added, — Theology, Law, Medicine and Philosophy. Preparation for these advanced courses is provided by the elementary and secondary schools, of which nearly two hundred and fifty are in operation. School attendance is compulsory for pupils between ten and fourteen years. The artistic tendencies, largely displayed in the past by silver filigree, are fostered by the sculpture gallery with its students, and by the national museum.

POPULATION

The physical features of Iceland force the inhabitants to the coasts, especially to the southwestern lowlands and the northwestern peninsula. Under changed conditions of life, there has been in late years a gradual drift to towns, and thus the aggregation of one third of the entire population of 100,000 is divided among seven places. The capital, Reykjavik, in 1925 had 22,022, Akreyri, Hafnarfjord, Vestmannaeyjar, 3,000 each. A score of other villages ranged from 500 to 2,200. Reykjavik has blossomed into quite a modern city, with its electric lights, movie theaters, accompanied by occasional short skirts and silk stockings of its bob-haired girls. The principal hotel provides jazz music in its dance room. Its university, museum and sculpture gallery are supplemented by other institutions of culture, all in buildings of modern construction. Even in the country sod huts are being replaced by houses of reënforced concrete.

The methods of oral and written communications are extended and efficient. There are 428 post-offices, with frequent and regular postal service. The telegraph installations, about two thousand miles in length, carry nearly six thousand miles of wire and reach almost every village. The introduction of the telephone has greatly relieved winter isolation; there are side branches from many exchanges, so that most farmers are in oral communication with their neighbors at will.

AGRICULTURE

By far the greater number have in the past lived by agriculture, which is an industry pursued under very adverse conditions. A sub-arctic climate limits rigidly the growth of grain and vegetables. Consequently hay and stock form the greater part of the produce. For food the people are obliged to import large quantities of potatoes and other fresh vegetables, local growth being unobtainable for lack of transportation. Meanwhile, under improved methods, the number of cattle, horses and sheep has increased fifty per cent. during this century. Under these improvements and those in fishing, the exports have increased the past twenty-seven years from $10 per head to $120 per head. The farmers appreciate the importance of coöperation, and at present there are more than one hundred societies who intelligently utilize economic methods. In order to introduce the most efficient processes, a school of husbandry has been opened at Hvanneyri, where practice and theory are combined.

In summer the students, under skilled supervision, are trained in farming methods of intensive and practical character. Their work covers modern dairying, stock raising, forage crops, and gardening. Heat has been introduced from the hot springs, and to-day in favored valleys there are raised good crops, — potatoes, turnips, cauliflowers, etc., and even tomatoes.

At present these pastures are covered by great herds of stock, including more than twenty thousand cows, and many thousand ponies, and more than a million sheep. These furnish large amounts of mutton and other meat for export.

FISHERIES

Fishing is the most important industry, and its methods have been greatly modified, with a corresponding increase in the product. This improvement has been incidentally the outcome of the

School of Navigation established in 1891, and the School of Marine Engineering in 1903. Highly specialized fishing is now done by motor boats, which in the past ten years have tripled in number. As a result the catch of the cod species has increased from fifteen million tons in 1900 to thirty-six million tons in 1922. Herring are also important, as their value was one third of the nearly sixty thousand tons of fish exported in 1923. It is interesting to note that no wage is paid to the fishermen, the industry being conducted by co-operation.

COMMUNICATIONS, LOCAL AND FOREIGN

Until the twentieth century, Iceland has been a land of isolation, where seven eighths of the people lived on farms, with no connecting roads, and the pony was the usual means of travel. To-day good roads and the motor car have given a new life to the people. At the end of 1924 there were 379 miles of carriage road ; in 1927 the systems were estimated to exceed 500 miles. In this extension many rapid rivers, formerly impassible in floods, are substantially bridged. A system of radiating roads, one seventy-two miles long, brings Reykjavik in direct connection with adjacent districts. Thingvellir, formerly isolated by an intervening desert, is now reached by a motor road which is traveled even in stormy winter weather, its high pillars, as guideposts, marking the roadway.

There is a radiating system of roads from Borganes, a port reached from the capital by weekly steamers.

Foreign travel was formerly possible about once in two months, but now foreign lines — British, Danish, Icelandic and Norwegian — make it possible to enter or leave Iceland twice a month.

The harnessing of the numerous waterfalls for the production of electric power has produced skilled electricians, who have built and manage the systems of city lighting, of industrial plants and the telegraph circuits now installed quite generally. The hot springs also furnish heat for bakeries, laundries and some of the large farmhouses. The utilization of these forces of nature has largely increased productivity and ameliorated domestic life. Iceland has now decided to increase its power largely.

For this purpose it has granted a concession of water power to a Norwegian company, which has contracted to construct an electric railway sixty miles in length, to connect the capital with the richest agricultural districts. The construction of the railway is to begin not later than May 1, 1929.

CHAPTER XII

SVALBARD

(*Formerly Spitsbergen*)

THIS archipelago, although having an area of only 25,000 square miles, is for several reasons the most interesting of arctic lands. Its situation is nearly intermediate between the Old and New worlds; its adjacent seas have contributed enormous wealth to the commercial world, and until the twentieth century its beautiful and accessible shores have remained uncolonized and its land resources unexploited. In turn claimed and abandoned by several nations, it recently became of such economic importance as to engage diplomatically the activities of seven nations to secure it a responsible government.

The conditions which led to its tutelage were set forth by an arctic expert, Sir Martin Conway. He said: "Dutchmen, Englishmen, Germans, Biscayans, Russians and Norwegians have all sought Spitsbergen for industrial purposes, and by their ruthless methods of extermination reduced it to its present almost lifeless condition. Unfortunately it continues to be a no-man's-land, annexed by no state and governed by no laws. Fisheries

are unregulated; there is no close time for bird
or beast, and so the animal depopulation threatens
to become complete. In the interests of science
and industry alike, it is time Spitsbergen were
annexed by some power capable of regulating
the country." Fortunately such action has been
taken, and the archipelago is now ruled by Norway.
It has been renamed Svalbard, though the separate
islands retain their former titles, as West Spitsbergen, Northeast Land, etc.

This result was brought about by the concerted
action of seven nations in the Treaty of Paris
February 9, 1920, ratified in 1923, by which the
sovereignty of the archipelago was conferred on
Norway. By Article I of the treaty:

"The High Contracting Parties undertake to
recognize, subject to the stipulations of the present
treaty, the full and absolute sovereignty of Norway
over the Archipelago of Spitsbergen, comprising,
with Bear Island or Beeren-Eiland, all the islands
situated between 10° and 35° longitude east of
Greenwich, and between 74° and 81° latitude
North, especially West Spitsbergen, Northeast
Land, Barents Island, Edge Island, Wiche Islands,
Hope Island or Hopen-Eiland, and Prince Charles
Foreland, together with all islands great or small,
and rocks appertaining thereto."

Under other articles are the following provisions:
Acquired rights are to be recognized, while pre-
existing claims are to be decided by a Danish

Commission; mining regulations drawn up by Norway must be approved by the contracting parties before enforcement, and such shall be equal; while the right to fish and hunt are open to the world, yet any measures enforced by Norway for the preservation of fauna and flora must be binding on all; recognized owners of land have exclusive right to hunt within a radius of 10 kilometres; taxes and restrictions must not exceed those of nations most favored by Norway; public wireless stations are open to all; an International Meteorological Station is to be established; the archipelago shall not be used for purposes of war.

EXPLORATIONS

Norwegian discovery having vanished in the mists of unrecorded history, Spitsbergen was rediscovered accidentally in 1596 by a Holland expedition, under Barents and Ryp. Seeking the Northeast Passage, they visited its west coast, where they reached a high latitude, 79° 42′ N.; they believed it to be a part of Greenland. The voyage of Henry Hudson, however, brought Spitsbergen into deserved prominence, when in 1607 he endeavored to reach China via the North Pole. He explored inlets and islands, among others Hakluyt Headland. He turned back after reaching latitude 80° 23′ N., by observation and 81° by dead reckoning; Conway questions seriously the accuracy of these latitudes, in his authoritative volume "No Man's Land," 1906. Hudson's voyage was of vast industrial importance, for his discovery of the numerous whales and walrus gave rise to the fisheries of the Greenland Sea (Chapter X). The claims, controversies and operations of the various whalers — Basques, Danish, English, French, Hollanders and Swedes — are set forth in detail by Conway. The commercial importance of the fishery may be estimated by the fact that in its flourishing condition about 400 ships and 20,000 men were engaged therein, and that in one year the Dutch catch was valued at about $1,250,000. Adventurous whalers visited all accessible inlets, and in this way the western and northern coasts, possibly Hinlopen Strait, were more or less accurately surveyed.

In 1610 Poole named Bell Sound, Ice Fiord and other adjacent points. Baffin, 1614, discovered Wiches Sound (Wilde Bay) and Sir Thomas Smith Inlet (Hinlopen Strait). Phipp's surveys, 1773, were inaccurate, says Beechey. Buchan and Franklin, 1818, made physical observations on Dane Island, where they were followed in 1824 by Clavering and Sabine.

Spitsbergen was first accurately described by Scoresby, 1823, in his "Polar Regions." Of it Grad says: "Scoresby surpasses in extent, variety and exactness everything written regarding the polar physics up to the beginning of the nineteenth century. Seventeen voyages to Spitsbergen ena-

bled this gifted observer to fully describe such phe-
nomena as are peculiar to these islands ; his book
yet remains the initial point of all scientific polar
search" (Grad : "Illes Spitsbergen." 1866).

In 1827 Parry, at Treurenberg Bay, made physical observations, while Keilhau studied the geology
of the southern coast. A French Commission,
1838, 1839, in the *Recherche* made extensive researches in and adjacent to Bell Sound and Magdalena Bay; Gaimard, Marmier, Bravais, Martin
and others participated. The studies of Martin
led to his brilliant generalizations on existing and
past floras (Gaimard : "Voyages en Scandinavie, en
Laponie, au Spitzberg." 1838. 16 vols., 6 atlases.
1843–1848).

Swedish researches in the archipelago have
added greatly to the world's knowledge of the
natural history and other branches of science.
They were made by nine expeditions between 1858
and 1896, which were initiated by Torrell. The
researches of this scientist, in the *Frithiof*, 1858,
resulted in his "Mollucsa-Fauna of Spitsbergen."
His associate Nordenskiold discovered rich, fossil-
bearing rocks in carboniferous formation. Renewing his researches in 1861, Torrell supplemented
his extensive geological investigations by much
additional data in various branches of natural
history. With Nordenskiold and Petersen he
explored Hinlopen Strait in a boat journey.
Meanwhile Chydenius made a successful survey

preparatory to measuring an arc of meridian. The expedition also visited the hitherto unexplored coast of Northeast Land, where they landed on the Seven Islands, and reached their farthest at Phipps Island, 80° 42′ N. Among their discoveries were Prince Oscar Land and two islands, — Charles XII and Lifeguard (Drabanten).

Nordenskiold led the expedition of 1864, with Duner and Malmgren, and covered Bell, Horn and Helis sounds, Stor Fiord, Edges and Barents lands. At Charles Foreland they providentially rescued a boatload of shipwrecked walrus-hunters, whose ship had been crushed by floes. As a result of this expedition Nordenskiold and Duner compiled a map, based on eighty different points, which had been determined by geodetic methods in this and other expeditions. It delineated Spitsbergen with an accuracy hitherto unattained in any arctic land.

The two north-polar Swedish expeditions of 1868 and 1872, organized through Nordenskiold, are described in Chapter XIX. Sweden maintained at Cape Thorsden (Chapter XX) an International Circumpolar Station in 1882–1883. The botanical researches of Nathorst and De Geer, 1882, were important. Nordenskiold, Jr., with Bjorling in 1890, studied glaciers between Horn Sound and Recherche Bay. In 1898 Nathorst, in the *Antarctica*, circumnavigated Spitsbergen, and visited King Charles and Giles Island. He also made geological investigations of Giles Island, which were a scientific success, as the island had been rarely seen, and never visited, since its discovery by Giles in 1707. Nathorst thus describes it: "It was glittering white; from its summit down to the sea not a rock projected. It presents a steep wall of ice to the waves, forming in some places big cubical icebergs." The island is in 80° 10′ N.

Swedish contributions to Spitsbergen literature fill some seven thousand pages of scientific memoirs and descriptive volumes. The results of these researches have been scientifically and materially beneficial. By their explorers the archipelago has been traversed, examined and charted in a most satisfactory manner. Its geology has been studied, its plant life classified — its flowering plants alone number 96 — and the location and features of many glaciers made known. Russian scientists have also contributed to research. Under Tchernychef, they coöperated in 1899, 1902 and since, with the Swedes, De Geer and Carlheim-Gyllenskold, in measuring a meridianal arc of 4 degrees 11 minutes, between 76° 38′ N. and 80° 47′ N. They also mapped extensive areas, and in geological researches delimited carboniferous, Silurian and Trias formations.

Otherwise the activities of the Russians and also of the Norwegians have been of an economic and material character, and are recited under Fur Industries later in this chapter.

English ventures in the Svalbard Archipelago during the nineteenth and twentieth centuries have been devoted to geographical or other scientific researches. In 1880 Leigh Smith, in his voyage to Franz Josef Archipelago, visited the north coasts of Spitsbergen and Northeast Land.

In 1896 the geographical explorations, which had been confined largely to the coasts, were extended to the interior. Sir Martin Conway, A. Trevor-Battye and E. J. Garwood made the first crossing of the island. Overland journeys were made from Advent Bay northeast to Van Mijen and Sassen bays, thence back via Agardh Bay. Nearly six hundred square miles of central Spitsbergen were surveyed, a region of alternating mountains and tundra valleys with fertile slopes, in striking contrast with the ice-capped coasts. Conway nearly circumnavigated the main islands, penetrated the great fiords, landed at Seven Islands and skirted Northeast Land between capes Platen and Mohn. The botanical, geological and zoological collections, supplemented by many photographs, added much to the physical knowledge of this arctic land (Conway: "First Crossing of Spitsbergen." 1897).

Conway and Garwood returned to Spitsbergen in 1898 to ascertain the extent of ice-capped areas in the interior. From the north arms of Ice Fiord they explored to the northeast and to the west. A glacier of 1,500 feet elevation was discovered near Chydeni Hill. From the Diadem, 4,150 feet high, were visible in all directions snowy hills, interlaced by *neves* and glaciers. Conway believes that, excepting New Friesland and Northeast Land, there are no extended areas covered by a continuous ice cap. These explorations had important bearing on the question of glacial action.

Especially important in extent and varied in research were the Oxford University expeditions between 1921 and 1924. The expedition of 1921 visited Bear Island, Ice Fiord, Prince Charles Foreland and Moffen Island. Biological in character, it made a general survey of the animals and plants of the west coasts. The Merton College expedition of 1923 extended the survey of animals and plants in the neighborhood of Liefde and Widje bays, on the islands and shores of Hinlopen Strait.

The expedition of 1924, under George Binney in the *Isbjorn* and *Oiland*, established a seaplane base in Liefde Bay, whence it made a survey of Northeast Land. Its aviation experiences are summarized in Chapter XVIII. While there were dangerous phases, the expedition was unusually successful. In its attempt from Hinlopen Strait to circumnavigate Northeast Land, the *Isbjorn* rounded Cape Mohn, 79° 18′ N., 25° 10′ E. and turning north skirted the ice-cliffed eastern shore to within twenty miles of Cape Leigh Smith. From Ulve Bay on the south coast to the 80th

parallel on the east coast, the shore presents continuous ice cliffs ranging from one hundred to
one hundred fifty feet high. At Cape Isis,
79° 42′ N., 26° 40′ E., there was an ice-free rock
spit where a sledge party landed. This party
under Binney crossed Northeast Land, August
5–15, to Wahlenberg Bay. Aldous, with another
sledge party, starting from the entrance to Wahlenberg Bay, reached Mt. Toil on the northwest
coast. The third party under Fraser attempted
to cross the island from west to east, but conditions
of travel and weather (they were held up by a
blizzard for sixty hours) obliged them to turn
back from 22° E., about one third across.

Among their results, besides ascertaining the
general condition of the main ice cap, was the
taking of aërial photographs of about seventy
miles of the coast line of Northeast Land (Binney: "With Seaplane and Sledge in the Arctic").

Valuable contributions were made in the
following papers: Elton, "The Biology in Relation
to the Geography"; Sanford, "Geology and
Glaciology"; Tymms, "Meteorology", also, "Aërial Survey"; Relf, "Magnetic Observations";
also "Wireless" (*Geographical Journal*, vol. xlvi).

POTENTIAL RESOURCES OF SVALBARD

The trend of material contributions to the
wealth of the world at large, by the arctic regions,
has widely differed in Svalbard from its course in

Alaska. In North America the Alaskan exploitation ran from furs to gold, and thence to fish and copper. In Svalbard the order was from sea to land, — first whales, then fur and now coal. Curiously enough, as Zordrager tells us, the earliest mineral exportation was mineral material from Alabaster Hook for use in the Delft porcelain factories.

FUR HUNTING

The utilization of the game resources of the land seems to have originated with the Russians, who, beginning hunting early in the eighteenth century, continued their pursuit well into the nineteenth century. The extent of their operations and the value of the production must have been very large in the aggregate. In "No Man's Land", *op. cit.*, Conway mentions thirty localities where existing remains of Russian huts indicate their occupation by hunters through the entire year. Their fortunes and misfortunes make stirring chapters in the book of human courage and endeavor, and are thought to have been initiated by the remarkable experiences of Himkof and his three comrades, who may well be called the Robinson Crusoes of the arctic. Marooned by the forced departure of their ship, while they were hunting, the fate of the Himkof party seemed sealed: They had only twelve rounds of ammunition, and food for a few days. It was six years (1743–1749) before a passing ship rescued the castaways; one, however, had died. The ingenuity, resourcefulness and industry of these Russian hunters had not only enabled them to clothe, shelter and feed themselves comfortably, but also to accumulate such store of furs as added materially to their wealth.

The Russian trappers who thereafter entered Spitsbergen came almost entirely from the regions bordering the White Sea. They hunted foxes and bears; reindeer escaped save for food, being of slight value in North Russia. Russian activities covered practically all ice-free regions: the furs were costly, for it is believed that during the two centuries of exploitation nearly one third of the hunters died of scurvy. One man, Starashchin, is said to have passed thirty-two years in Spitsbergen, fifteen consecutively without leaving the archipelago.

Norwegian activities have been of a minor order and of a material character. Their ventures assumed a certain importance about 1830, when failure of land game caused the withdrawal of the Russians. However, there had been more or less Norwegian voyages, since venturesome mariners of Hammerfest entered the adjacent seas, and began hunting and fishing along the coasts. At first the Norwegians confined their efforts to the capture of seals, walrus and white whales. Later they found the land game more profitable, and particularly the reindeer, as the meat grew in demand at home. This became an important factor in the prosperity of the northwestern ports of Norway. The activity of these hunters was such as steadily diminished the wild life of Svalbard. The vast inroads made on the game of the archipelago is shown by the products or thirty-one hunting sloops from Tromsoe alone, which in 1906 brought back 9,460 pelts, of which no less than 2,888 were of reindeer. Fortunately game restrictions are now in force.

On the subject, Rudmose Brown, "The Polar Regions", 1927, says: "In Spitsbergen the work of the Norwegian hunters and trappers, and Sportsmen of many nations, has almost exterminated the reindeer. The Spitsbergen hunters used to take some 3,000 head a year 80 years ago; latterly a few dozen was a good bag. . . . Fortunately for its hope of survival the reindeer is now protected by Norway; none may be shot until 1934. . . . The destruction of the fox has been so complete that where 20 years ago foxes swarmed in hundreds, not one is now to be seen and the bark is seldom heard; it is now protected by law. . . . The polar bear is becoming quite rare. . . . Walrus and eiderduck are to be protected on all the islands of Svalbard, and the number of hunters allowed is to be limited so as to prevent excessive inroads on the game."

MINERAL RESOURCES

Geological surveys have disclosed the existence of the following minerals: asbestos, coal, copper, gypsum, iron, marble, mica, phosphate rock and zinc; of these coal alone is of present value. In 1872 a Swedish company attempted the mining of the phosphate deposits at Cape Thorsden. A house was built, a small railway constructed and mining was commenced. It speedily developed that the venture was unprofitable and it was abandoned. Coal mining has become the principal industry, although it is possible that some day the large deposits of pure gypsum may be utilized.

THE COAL INDUSTRY

The presence of coal has been known nearly three centuries. From time to time small amounts of surface deposits were collected, and some small cargoes were occasionally carried to Europe.

At the beginning of the twentieth century there were several ventures in mining, but they were economic failures. About 1904 two coal mines were opened at Advent Bay. The English company found poor coal on the east shore, and failed. The mine on the west shore proved to be of better quality, and under an American, Longyear, a successful mine was put in operation. This success induced other nationalities to exploit such extensive outcrops as promised large returns with a minimum of labor. While coal is widely distributed in the archipelago, the most extensive beds are on the shores of Ice Fiord; large amounts are also found in Lowe Sound and at Kings Bay.

As far as determined there are more than ten thousand million tons, *in situ*, of which nearly three quarters is of the tertiary formation, — an excellent steam coal of high quality. About one sixth are carboniferous beds, mainly good coking coal. The remainder is cretaceous coal, an inferior grade with much ash (Rudmose Brown : "Polar Regions." 1927).

Mining activities are practically centered in Ice Fiord, where the following mines have been operated : Cape Boheman, Dutch-Norwegian, abandoned; Barentsburg, Dutch at Green Harbor; Grumant, Anglo-Russian, at Coles Bay; Hjorthamn, Norwegian, east side of Advent Bay; Longyear, Norwegian, west side Advent Bay. At Kings Bay is the Ny-Aalesund Norwegian mine, and at the head of Lowe Sound is Sveagruvan, a Swedish mine on Braganza Bay. There is also to be mentioned Bruce City, Klaas Billen Bay, Ice Fiord, a Scotch mine which is soon to be worked. There are nearly a dozen other preempted coal beds, some abandoned as unprofitable, others in preparation for mining.

Work continues throughout the year, and storage bins of a capacity of about two hundred thousand tons hold the winter product, since freight boats run only six or seven months in the year. To increase the output the best modern machinery and appliances have been installed at the largest mines. These include coal cutters, electric traction, and cable conveyers. At some mines a large collier can be loaded in less than a day. The exportation of coal has assumed quite large amounts, 451,914 tons in 1924, and 413,412 tons in 1925. It is asserted that it will soon reach half a million tons (Dole: "Americans in Spitsbergen", 2 v. 1922).

At each mine ample provisions are made for the health, comfort and recreation of the miners and their families. At Longyear City especially, besides comfortable, centrally-heated dwellings, there are schools, hospital, church and theater. A radio station keeps the community in direct communication with the outside world, and the Norwegian Government provides a good mail service.

Bear Island has ample coal, and some galena which promises successful exploitation. The Ostervaag mine has been worked intermittently, but awaits better conditions for resumption.

Spitsbergen in the past has been reached in summer only and by steamer, but the amazing flight by airplane of Wilkins and Eielson, in April, 1928, from Point Barrow to Svalbard, shows it accessible during the entire year. Their non-stop flight of 2,200 miles was made in twenty and a half hours.

CHAPTER XIII

POLAR EUROPE

EXPLOITATION of arctic lands in extreme Northern Europe has continued, though irregularly, despite economic and political disturbances; it demands brief consideration. European Russia is considered in connection with its great outlying archipelago, Novaya Zemlya, in Chapter XV.

POLAR NORWAY

The history of the Scandinavian people is of deep interest to all who honor men moved by a spirit of adventure and endowed with resolute courage to face and conquer adverse conditions of nature. Rarely has any race equalled and none surpassed this folk along these lines. Through the past five hundred years their changes in life-methods have been slow and conservative, since Magnus Olaus in his "History of the Northern Nations", Rome, 1554, picturesquely outlined them.

Confined to a narrow region, nowhere exceeding two hundred fifty miles in width, Norway faces tempestuous seas, bordering the arctic circle. Its people have prospered on wealth wrested from the ocean, rather than on the productions of an unfriendly soil.

[137]

Hammerfest, in 70° 04′ N., is the most northerly city of the continental world, and from its remote locality might be thought inactive and somnolent. Yet it has replaced by its 3,210 inhabitants the arctic activities long fostered by the British. Here largely center the sea-oil industries, dependent on the thousands of mariners who seek cod and other fish. It has also built up and conducts a large trade with the people of the White Sea regions. Nearly destroyed by fire in 1890, the city was promptly rebuilt along modern lines. Alive to the march of progress elsewhere, it harnessed its neighboring waterfall, and set an example to all Norway by being the first city of that country to be lighted by electricity.

The most remote of arctic towns are Vardo and Vadso, north of the 70th parallel, situated at the mouth of Varanger Fiord, on the shores of Barents Sea. Along the north shore of the fiord is a road of 130 miles, which connects Vardo with the Tana-Karasjok road in the interior. Vardo (population 3,488) is one of the few arctic ports that is open the entire year, which makes it an important business center. It has a British consul, a customs officer, county medical officer, hospital and newspaper; it enjoys frequent steamer service with Southern Norway. This polar outpost, one of the most northerly in the world, is the principal factor in controlling the trade with North Finland, and in exploiting the resources of Barents Sea. The adjacent town of Vadso (2,067 inhabitants) is almost as important as Vardo, and is likewise favored by officials and trading firms.

Tromso, in 69° 38′ N., with 10,070 inhabitants, is the principal city of arctic Norway. Treeless and barren inland, it looks to the sea for its prosperity. The adjacent waters are rich in fish, and along the neighboring fiords and sounds the Norwegian fishermen to the number of many thousands are engaged in the catch. At Tromso all the operations for the utilization of the fish are carried on. It is also the principal port for the Svalbard (Spitsbergen) trade, which is increasing in value, although along new lines. Its other industries are tanneries, furs and boat-building. It is a thriving town, modern in construction and in its life methods.

International coöperation with Sweden has materially benefited arctic Norway, particularly in perfecting the cross-country railway system from Luela, Gulf of Bothnia, to Narvik, Norway, 68.5° N., on Ofotenfiord. The Norwegian branch of thirty miles connects Narvik with Riksgransen at the Swedish border. By this system hundreds of thousands of tons of Swedish iron ore are shipped yearly to Great Britain and continental Europe.

It is needless to dwell in detail on Trondhjem (Drontheim), a city of 53,225 inhabitants a few miles south of the arctic circle. It is a modern

city, the center of several railway systems — one
built in this decade to Sunna on the arctic circle,
— with public buildings, industrial establishments,
port facilities, etc., befitting the standards of this
century. It is here mentioned to illustrate the
spirit of Norwegian activity, which covers the
whole of Norway.

ARCTIC FINLAND

The world has awaited with interest to learn
the future policies and business development of
the new member of the family of nations, — Finland. It is the only republic in Europe bordering
on the northern sea. Seventh in area among the
European countries, its population of more than
three millions promises to make its great natural
wealth contributory to the world.

Fortunately its Minister of Foreign Affairs has
realized the advantage of making known to other
nations its possibilities, — economic and material
("Finland: The Country, Its People and Institutions." 1926).

The wooded wealth of Finland is enormous, as
more than one half of its soil is covered by fine
forests, one quarter within the arctic zone. While
its greatest industry is agricultural, increasing
activity is shown in the exploitation of its forests.
The income from the state forests alone amounted
to more than sixty million dollars in 1924. The
exports are principally timber, wood pulp, cellulose

and other similar articles. The shipments of timber rose from $765,000,000 in 1923 to $815,000,000 in 1924, with a similar increase in values of wood pulp and other like articles.

To ensure winter exports from the central provinces, methods have been adopted to keep the Gulf of Finland open by ice breakers. Should continued success be impracticable, Finland contemplates the possibility of being forced to construct a railway to its single ice-free port in Petsamo Fiord, Barents Sea, as Russia has done in building its railroad to Murmansk. Fortunately Finland secured by its treaty with Soviet Russia, in 1920, the Petsamo district, which borders Barents Sea. While Finland has rail communication with the Atlantic via Luela, Sweden, and Narvik, Norway, successful export trade depends on cheap water transportation.

Nearly one third of Finland is within the arctic circle, a section that is thinly populated. The principal inhabitants are Lapps, who numbered by the last census about 2,150; intermingled are Carelians, Russians and Norwegians. In the northerly portions there are many small farms, where stock and poultry are kept. While in the lake region there are many Lapps who live principally by fishing, the majority adhere to their former life in the north.

On the shores of Barents Sea, the majority of the populations are the nomadic reindeer-breeding

[141]

Lapps. By contact with other races they have modified their methods of living, no longer trading by barter, and under changed conditions have adopted many of the modern accessories of life.

However, they live on the reindeer, moving and seeking good pasturage in summer, and rounding them up for branding the young and for sale in the autumn. Under changed conditions the number of the reindeer are decreasing. Even the Lapps are becoming less individualistic, having formed about sixty organizations for the control of the reindeer industry. Rules have been established and are enforced by provincial governors, herd managers and the registrar who records the earmarks for identification. Reindeer meat is shipped to adjacent markets, and when the markets are distant the meat is smoked, to meet the popular demand. The Lapp women use the pelts for boots, shoes and coats. The bones are utilized for knife handles and ornaments.

Coöperation has greatly benefited the dairy industry, through improvement of the cattle, and by the introduction of methods which have increased the quantity and raised the quality of butter and cheese. In this most important agricultural industry, a controlling factor is the Valio Butter Exporting Society, with which the greater number of the six hundred coöperating dairies are associated. Organized in 1905, the Valio Society exported in 1925 butter to the value

RESIDENTIAL QUARTER OF REYKJAVIK, ICELAND.

DAIRY FARM IN ARCTIC FINLAND.

of 604,400,000 Finnish marks. The character of the dairy farms in Northern Finland is indicated by the accompanying illustration.

It will be many years before the arctic provinces are developed. However, the four thousand coöperative societies are a potent element, capable of phenomenal exploitation.

POLAR SWEDEN

The greatest advance in the twentieth century, in utilizing the natural resources of a polar environment, is that made by Sweden, in its so-called Norrland. Half a century ago it was described as a barren and worthless region, a conglomeration of dense forests, wastes of bogs, and rugged mountains. Its few inhabitants were nomadic, wandering, Mongolian Lapps, differing in race and language from the Swedes. Wise policies and intelligent action have transformed this remote and desolate arctic region into a field of beneficent and flourishing activity.

The natural resources of Norrland are iron ore, forests and waterfalls. Its iron-ore deposits are excellent in quality and enormous in amount. The two fields now mined are Gallivare, estimated deposit of two hundred seventy million tons, and the iron mountain Kirunavaara, seven hundred fifty million tons. For the development of these ores an arctic railway was completed in 1923, connecting Luela with Narvik, Norway, so that

[143]

exports could be made either via the Gulf of Bothnia or the Atlantic Ocean.

Since 1900 there has grown up at the Kirunavaara mines the phenomenal city of Kiruna. It has all modern conveniences, electrical and otherwise. Its church is ornamented with beautiful sculpture and paintings. This community, near 68° N., is a striking illustration of the wonderful exploitation of arctic resources.

The ultimate prosperity of the industry turned on the utilization of the vast water power of Norrland, thus replacing the expensive imported coal. At Porjus Falls was erected the largest power plant in Sweden, where is generated 82,500 horse power, to be prospectively raised to 140,000 horse power. To overcome arctic disadvantages the power plant was installed 165 feet below ground level. From this plant the Luela-Narvik system was electrified, the first great railway in Europe to be operated by electricity. A dam 4,115 feet long and 42 high ensures water in the coldest weather.

The forestal resources of Norrland are enormous in extent, and consist of excellent spruce and pine. The methods of water transportation are so favorable that land transport averages less than five miles to floating channels. These conditions have developed an enormous industry of wood pulp and other paper goods. The beneficent results of these developments to Sweden are shown by the reports of 1924, when the percentages of all exports were

KIRUNA, THE IRON MOUNTAIN OF SWEDEN, NEAR 68° N. IN OPERATION
DURING THE ENTIRE ABSENCE OF THE SUN, IN THE POLAR NIGHT.

divided as follows : Wood pulp, etc., 28, timber 21 and minerals 9.

Norrland is thus becoming a land of thriving communities, one town, Kiruna, having ten thousand inhabitants. Agriculture, being unprofitable, is replaced by cattle-breeding, while the wandering Lapps find a good market for their reindeer and have commenced to have glass windows in their turf dirt-covered huts, and use alarm clocks and sewing machines as signs of a new life.

Of the changes a Swedish writer, Stiernstedt, says : "Northern Sweden, long neglected, is in process of becoming our richest treasure. The leading materials, iron of the very best quality, and forests cultivated scientifically, are attracting crowds of workmen. White coal as a motive force is there available. The electric current created by its torrential waterfalls would furnish electricity to the whole country at quite a small cost. Special enterprises for manufacturing cellulose, wood pulp, steel, etc., are contributing to transform the arctic regions, hitherto deserts, into civilized districts covered with roads. This in a section where formerly there was only one person to a square kilometre."

CHAPTER XIV

FRANZ JOSEF ARCHIPELAGO

PETERMANN says : "I consider it highly probable that the great Arctic pioneer, William Baffin, may have seen the western shores of Franz Josef Land in 1614." However that may be, the first definite knowledge of these islands is due to the exertions of the Austrian soldier Payer, and the English yachtsman Leigh Smith.

At the instance of Lieutenant Carl Weyprecht, two expeditions were outfitted by Count Wilczek to explore Novaya Zemlya and attempt the North-east Passage. The expedition of 1871, in the *Isbjorn*, reached 78° 48′ N., 42° E. In 1872 Wilczek in the *Isbjorn* landed supplies for an emergency on Barents Island, while the main expedition sailed on the *Tegetthof*, with Weyprecht in command; with him was Lieutenant Julius Payer, who was to explore any land that might be discovered.

Steaming north on August 20, the ship was beset the same day in 76° 22′ N., 63° E., within sight of Novaya Zemlya. Subject to wind and current the *Tegetthof* drifted with the main pack, from which she was destined never to escape. Threatened with shipwreck from violent movements of .

the surrounding floes, the men built a house on the ice, in which were stored supplies for use in emergency. However, the winter passed with the ship still safe. From February, 1873, the drift was first northwest, then north to their greatest longitude, 71° E., in 79° N.; with summer the drift changed to westward to 59° 05' E., nearly the most westerly point.

The monotony of the drift for a year was broken on August 30, 1873, when with rising mist there was seen far to the northeast the bold outlines of land. It was hailed with enthusiasm, for it was realized that their sufferings had not been in vain, since they had added a new land to the known domain of the world. At the end of September an unsuccessful attempt was made to visit an island (Hochstetter). Stable ice conditions enabled them to reach Wilczek Island in November.

The second winter passed without notable incident, the ship remaining nearly stationary. In March, 1874, land explorations began, when Payer visited Hall Island, but the intense cold, 59 degrees below zero, frosted the men badly and obliged their return. The main journey began March 26, when Payer started north with ten men and three dogs. Despite the rough ice, violent blizzards and low temperatures, the party reached Austria Sound on April 1, and on account of the exhaustion of two men they camped for a week on Hohenloe Island, 81° 37' N. Determined to continue his explorations, Payer left the two disabled men in charge of a selected man and started north. In crossing Middendorf glacier a snow bridge broke through. Dragged in harness to the edge of the crevasse, Payer was saved by the wedging of the sledge, but Zaninovich was thrown down with the dogs on to an ice ledge. Payer ran in his stocking feet through the deep snow several miles to Hohenloe Island, and returning with a relief party succeeded in drawing up from the crevasse both Zaninovich and the dogs, fortunately un-injured. Proceeding, Payer reached, on April 12, 1874, Cape Fligely, 81° 51′ N., which was the most northerly known land in the Old World, and yet remains so. Prevented from going farther by open water, Payer was deceived by mirage into the belief that there was land to the north, but the explorations of his successors in Franz Josef Archipelago show that this section of the Arctic Ocean is entirely landless.

The pack remaining unbroken, the *Tegetthof* was abandoned on May 20, 1874, and the crew reached Novaya Zemlya on August 24.

De Bruyne in the *Willem Barents* sighted land, probably Northbrook Island, in 1879, but the archipelago was not revisited until the voyage of the English yachtsman Leigh Smith in the *Eira*, during 1880. Falling in with the pack in 77° 10′ N., 40° E., the yacht was driven hither and thither. Smith discovered on August 14 May Isle, southwest of McClintock Island. Pushing his explorations with sound judgment and great energy, he covered the whole southwestern coast from 42° E., to 54° E., the most westerly point of the south shores seen by Payer. The surveys of Smith extended from McClintock Island to Cape Neale, covering not only the main shore but the fringe of outlying islands. Included were Brady, Northbrook, Hooker and other small islands, Nightingale and other sounds. A secure harbor (Eira) was located in 80° 04′ N., 48° 40′ E. From his most northerly point 80° 19′ N., 44° 52′ E., it was seen that the western coast (Alexandra Land) trended north-northwest. After skirting the coast easterly to Wilczek Island, the *Eira* withdrew, with valuable botanical and geological collections from the archipelago, and marine life from the adjacent seas. Smith renewed his explorations in 1881, but the *Eira* was lost and he was obliged to winter, which was done comfortably, — the first land wintering in the archipelago; the party reached Novaya Zemlya safely in August, 1882 (Payer: "New Lands within the Arctic Circle." 2 vols., 1876).

The voyages made by Smith were valuable in their results. They not only extended far to the northwest of Franz Josef Archipelago, but disclosed the comparative richness of its fauna and flora. They also brought forward prominently this region as a suitable base, whence extended journeys could be made safely northward by a properly equipped and well-led party, while a safe retreat to Novaya Zemlya was practicable (*Proceedings Royal Geographical Society*, 1881 and 1883).

The very valuable hydrographic and physical explorations of the Norwegian North-Atlantic Expedition, 1876 (Mohn *et al.* "Den Norske Nordhavens-Expedition." 1883), in the Spitsbergen and Barents seas stimulated further scientific researches in arctic waters. From 1878 Holland sent out for many summers the *Willem Barents* for work in Barents Sea, with most gratifying and valuable results. The investigations extended almost to the southern shores of the archipelago.

The expedition fitted out by Alfred Harmsworth in 1894 was conducted by Frederick Jackson, who established his base at Cape Flora, whence he planned a thorough exploration of the archipelago. The *Windward*, sent back by him, had an unfortunate voyage of sixty-five days through adverse ice conditions and reached Vardo, Norway, with twelve sick and two dead of scurvy. Ice conditions prevented the annual visit to Cape Flora in 1895 of the *Windward*, but her voyages in 1896 and in 1897 (when Jackson returned) were successful.

The extensive journeys of Jackson covered nearly fifteen degrees of longitude, from 42° E. to 56° E., and eighty miles of latitude, from Northbrook Island, south of the 80th parallel to 81° 20' N. In 1895 by a boat journey, involving

Photograph by A. Fiala

STEAMER AMERICA IN 82° 04′, AUGUST 31, 1903. FIALA-ZIEGLER EXPEDITION
TO FRANZ JOSEF LAND, 1903–05.

great danger, he reached on the northwestern coast Cape Mary Harmsworth, in 80° 30′ N., 42° 30′ E. On March 18, 1896, from Cape Richtofen, 80° 50′ N. 54° E., Victoria Sea to the northwest was seen to be dotted here and there with islands. In 1897 Alexandra Land was rounded, and by a journey across its extensive ice cap, Cape Mary Harmsworth was found to be its most westerly point. After the arrival of Nansen Jackson abandoned his efforts to reach a high latitude (Jackson: "Thousand Days in the Arctic." 1899).

The extended geographical explorations of Jackson were supplemented by physical observations and collections, which give an adequate idea of the fauna, flora and other physical characteristics of the Franz Josef Archipelago.

The existence of Victoria, White and Great islands in Victoria Sea quite conclusively proves the former unity of the archipelagoes of Svalbard (Spitsbergen) and Franz Josef.

Nansen in his return from his north-polar expedition via Franz Josef Archipelago (Chapter XIX) discovered White Land, — a group of five islands north of Graham Bell Island; also islands off Prince Rudolf Island. His scientific researches in these regions have been published in "Scientific Results of the Nansen Expedition." Vol. 1.

The northern limits of the archipelago were determined by the north-polar expedition (Chapter XIX) of the Duke of the Abruzzi, 1900–1901. The

Stella Polare, after attaining 82° 04′ N., 59° E., anchored in Zeplitz Bay, 81° 47′ N. The observations of the Duke prove the nonexistence of Petermann and King Oscar lands, reported by Payer, whose Cape Fligely was found to be in 81° 51′ N. The duke describes Franz Josef Archipelago as being almost completely glacier-covered; only five per cent. of the land is ice-free. While he eliminated islands reported east of Rudolf Island, yet Whitney and other islands of Wellman, 1898, remain to his credit (Wellman: *National Geographic Magazine*, 1902).

Wellman's work resulted in the exploration of the extreme easterly islands. Baldwin, his assistant in a long sledge trip, determined the eastern boundary of Wilczek Island, and discovered a number of islands, of which Graham Bell is the largest, extending to 81° 26′ N., and 65° E., the eastern limit. Renewed efforts in 1900 had scanty results.

The Fiala-Zeigler expeditions of 1901 and 1903–1905 were important for the scientific observations, especially by Peters, in magnetism, which were exceptionally valuable from systematic methods and completeness of record. Their ship, *America*, attained 82° 04′ N., an unusual latitude, but was crushed wintering in Teplitz Bay. This prevented extended sledging commenced by Fiala.

The British Arctic Expedition of 1925, under Worsely and Algarsson, made valuable hydro-

[152]

graphic observations in the seas around Franz
Josef and Northeast lands (Worsely: "Under
Sail in the Frozen North").

The disastrous north-polar expeditions of Sedoff
and Broussilov are noted in Chapter XIX.

CHAPTER XV

NOVAYA ZEMLYA AND NORTHERN RUSSIA

THE material resources of the inhabitants of Northern Russia have always been fish and furs, principally from White and Barents seas and their bordering lands. The exploitation of the sea fisheries and land game were local industries, until the explorations for the Northeast Passage in the mid-sixteenth century caused the trade and activities connected therewith to become international.

Thence arose the great Muscovy Company, from which England and Russia largely profited, which caused the phenomenal rise of Archangel from a fishing village to a sub-arctic metropolis. As the economic value of local arctic resources became known, the intelligent officials of Russia took action to control, by exploration and occupation, the islands of Barents Sea. These historical expeditions are worthy of note, and especially the trade development, since its importance is not generally recognized.

THE WHITE SEA REGIONS

International participation in the trade of Arctic Russia was initiated by the efforts of England, in

1553, to reach Cathay by the Northeast Passage. Sir Hugh Willoughby, in the *Esperanza*, and *Bona Confidentia*, reached and wintered at the mouth of the Varzina, on the barren coast of Kola Peninsula, where he and his seventy-four comrades perished of scurvy. His more fortunate associate, Richard Chancellor, wintered in the *Edward Bonaventure* at the mouth of the Dwina, and established friendly relations with the Russian officials. Of Chancellor's voyage, Nordenskiöld said, "Incalculable was the influence upon English commerce and on the development of the whole of Russia, and of the north of Norway. From the monastery at the mouth of the Dwina a flourishing town (Archangel) has arisen and a numerous population has settled on the coast of the Polar Sea."

Until the end of the seventeenth century all trans-oceanic trade with Russia was transacted over the White Sea route. Under Peter the Great, Archangel enjoyed marked prosperity, and the building of Russian ships began for local transportation. The upbuilding of St. Petersburg led to commercial jealousies and resulted in the imposition of restrictions to the advantage of shipments via the Baltic.

While this official action adversely affected the arctic route, and caused a notable decline in Archangel, a struggle against economic methods could not permanently last. The local hemp industry was greatly stimulated through the action of the Russian Government in developing its culture, and in the establishment of rope walks; the first opened was by the English at Kholmogry near Archangel.

Later, rapidly growing amounts of agricultural products of the southern regions overwhelmed the facilities at Archangel. In the nineteenth century, as a remedy, a narrow-gauge railway was built from Moscow, via Volgoda, to Archangel. This brought the basin of the Volga in direct relation with the desirable and economical sea route. However, the closed season, when the White Sea was ice-bound, limited the amount of freight that could be transported over this route.

At the beginning of the World War, enormous demands were made on this system, which caused Russia to plan the construction of another arctic railway, parallel to and west of the existing line, to Kem on the White Sea. Wisely the railway was extended to connect Petrograd (Leningrad) with the Arctic Ocean. It runs through Kem and Kandalaksha, a thriving fishing settlement, across the Kola Peninsula, terminating on the Murman coast at Katyarina Harbor, a port (Murmansk) ice-free the entire year. Data are now unavailable as to the values of Russian exports over these two routes. By the last published reports there was shipped from Archangel alone one million tons of lumber in a single year. In the not distant future exports from Arctic Russia must largely increase.

NOVAYA ZEMLYA

The two largest islands of this archipelago, separated by the narrow strait of Matochkin Shar, are known as Novaya Zemlya. Frequented by Russian fishermen in the earlier centuries, they became known to the world at large by the voyage of Stephen Burrough in the *Searchthrift*, 1556, in which he discovered Waigat Strait. He fell in with a Russian fisherman, Loshak, who said, "This land is called Novaya Zemlya, that is to say The New Land." Pet, 1580; Hudson, 1607; Wood, 1676, visited its waters but made no landing.

The earliest explorations were by the Dutch expedition of 1594, 1595 and 1596. Barents in 1594 reached Orange Island, north of the 77th parallel, and in 1595 turned back from the Waigat. In 1596 he rounded the northern island, and sailing south along the east coast was forced to enter Ice Haven, August 26. There the personnel wintered in a house built on shore. Extreme cold, violent blizzards and other unfavorable conditions caused the death of two men and the illness of many. With coming spring the ship was still icebound and affairs were desperate. It was decided that the only chance of safety was by a retreat in small boats to Lapland, a thousand miles distant. The journey was made safely, but on June 20, 1597, near North Cape, this great navigator died. Of him Beke says, in De Veer's "Three Voyages of

Barents" (Hakluyt Society, 1875), "Barents made so many discoveries and traced so large an extent of coast, both of Spitsbergen and Novaya Zemlya, that the surveys of all of the whole of our recent explorers (1853) put together are insufficient to identify all the points visited by him." It was nearly two centuries before a successor surpassed Barents in those seas. It was two hundred seventy-five years before Ice Haven was again visited by Elling Carlsen in 1871. He was followed by M. Gundersen in 1875, and by C. L. W. Gardner in 1876. All confirm the accuracy of the Dutch navigator.

Many hunters, fishermen and scientists visited Novaya Zemlya in the nineteenth century. Palliser in 1869 sailed thirty miles north of Cape Nassau. In the *Diana*, Wiggin reached 76° N. Quale and Ulve, 1870, made notable voyages. E. H. Johannsen was given the silver medal of the Swedish Academy of Science for hydrographical observations in Barents and Kara seas in 1869. In the following years he discovered and circumnavigated in 77° 31′ N., 86° E., a small island (Lonely), snow-free, frequented by bears, birds and seals. Booth visited the archipelago in 1879 and made collections (Markham, "Polar Reconnaisance." 1881). Fielden and Pearson, in 1895 and 1897, made botanical and geological studies at Paktusof Island, 74° 24′ N. More important have been Russian investigations and activities.

SAMOYED ALEXANDER VILKA AND HIS FAMILY, KRESTOVAIA BAY, N. Z.

SAMOYED SUMMER HUNTING CAMP, PUKH BAY, BARENTS SEA.

RUSSIA IN NOVAYA ZEMLYA

Hunters and fishermen frequented the islands early in the sixteenth century. Often they wintered, as Barents (1596) found crosses of the old believers at Krestovoi (Cross) Islands, while at Mutchnoi (Flour) Island were sacks of flour in an abandoned Russian hut; also remains of small boats. In 1760 Sava Loghkin passed two winters there, and circumnavigated the southern island, it is claimed. In 1768–1769 Rosmislov explored the region of Matochkin Shar, and there wintering lost his ship. Lutke, 1821–1824, explored the west coast. He charted accurately the southern coast lines, and made valuable observations in astronomy and hydrography. Between 1832 and 1834 Paktusof surveyed the east coast as far north as Paktusof Islands, 74° 24′ N. He wintered twice and made extensive observations in astronomy, geodesy, meteorology and hydrography; few have done better work with equal means. The voyage of Zivolka, 1837 and 1838, made many contributions through his geologist, Lehmann, and naturalist, Von Baer. Zivolka's imperfect map omitted the extreme northern portions. Baer's generalization on the eastern Polar Seas and his geographical elucidations were so misleading as to lead to errors only lately eliminated from our charts.

The Russian International Polar Station (Chapter XX), under Lieutenant C. Andrejeff, 1882–

1883, was located on the west coast at Little Karmakuli, Moller Bay, 72° 23′ N., 52° 44′ E. It
resulted not only in the accumulation and discussion of magnetic, meteorological and hydrographic
conditions, but also of the fauna and flora of
the southern isle and of the geography of the
interior, through the travels of Doctor Grinewet-
sky (Andrejeff and Lenz: "Beobachtungen der
Russischen Polarstation auf Nowaja Semla."
2 vols. 1886–1891). In 1896 Prince Golitzin established a meteorological station at Malye (Little)
Karmakuli.

Between 1887 and 1891, Nissilof passed three
winters on the southern island, making valuable
scientific collections in the interior; he also discovered three islands near the coast. (Paschoff:
"Nissilov's Voyage à la Nouvelle-Zemble." *Tour
du Monde*. 1894). The voyage of Engelhardt and
Chernysteff in 1895 and the eclipse expedition of
1896 also contributed important physical data.
In late years, Vilitski and Vafnek made extensive
hydrographic surveys along the coasts. Borisoff,
in his expedition of 1901–1902, lost his ship, but in
a sledge journey of one hundred six days in the
interior discovered many rivers and lakes, previously unknown.

THE COLONIZATION OF THE ARCHIPELAGO

The islands have doubtless been intermittently
inhabited by Russian hunters, Samoyeds or Pom-

eranians, since the fifteenth century. Scarcity of
game in bad seasons often caused the hunters
to return to the continent to avoid starvation,
from which at least one family perished.

Activities during the past one hundred years
have become available through the courtesy of the
Russian Geographical Society, in a report made to
its president, J. C. Schokalsky, by R. Samoilovitch
of the Arctic Institute.

In the seventeenth and eighteenth centuries,
nomadic hunters pursued game every summer.
Isolated parties at times remained on the southern island for several winters, suffering hardships
and occasionally perishing. Paktusof records
the tragic fate of the family of the Samoyed Virey,
living at Loginov Bay, which died of starvation.

Nevertheless the game attracted hunters and
traders in larger numbers, and Voronin states that
in 1835 thirteen Russian ships were engaged in
the industry; as they often suffered disaster from
the violent storms, the government built a refuge
hut at Kostin Shar in 1870. In 1877 a life-saving
station was constructed at Little Karmakuli,
Moller Bay, with Pilot Tiagyn in charge. These
houses were occupied in 1878–1879 by a part of the
forty-two permanent inhabitants, among whom
was Vilka, who had lived there since 1869. This
was the first colony. In 1900 an assistant surgeon was stationed there for medical aid, and a
chapel built whose deacon was obligated to teach

reading and writing. In 1896 Prince Golitzin established there a meteorological station.

Another colony was located on the southern island, at the western entrance to Matochkin Shar. In 1923 there were established on the northern island, at the eastern mouth of Matochkin Shar, a radio station and geo-physical observatory. From them weather reports are daily given to the world. In 1910 the fourth colony was founded on Krestovaia Bay. At this post there was built a dwelling house, a chapel, a barn and a bathhouse.

A house was also built at Russanovo, Pukhovaia Bay, and at Krassino (Black Bay), each occupied by a Russian family.

In 1927 the permanent inhabitants in Novaya Zemlya numbered forty-nine Russians and one hundred thirty Samoyeds. They were distributed as follows: Krassino, nine Russians; Russanovo, eight Russians; Cross Bay, three Russians, twenty-seven Samoyeds; Matochkin Shar, three Russians, thirty-two Samoyeds; Karmakuli, twenty-one Russians, twenty-seven Samoyeds; Belushaia Bay, five Russians, forty-four Samoyeds. The nomadic summer hunters, in considerable numbers, vary from year to year.

Every post in addition to its dwelling houses has a bathhouse, and a Russian stove which is heated by wood brought from Archangel. All stations are visited twice each year, in July and September, by government steamships.

Land transportation is by dogs, who are largely fed on dovekies. At sea small boats are in general use, though motor boats have been introduced at Black Bay and Matochkin Shar.

The game includes bears, foxes, eiders, *goletz* (fish), geese, sea dogs, seals, walrus and white whales. The Samoyed communities are under Ilya Vilk, an intelligent and literate Samoyed, who is entitled an executive commissioner.

He in turn receives his instructions from the Administration of Insular Possessions at Archangel. This administration is the outcome of the active policy of the Soviet Government to develop the material resources of Polar Russia. On June 30, 1924, the Soviet Government at Moscow issued a decree centralizing under one head its varied activities. A bureau was established at Archangel, charged with the administration and exploitation of all the Russian polar islands.

PRODUCTS OF THE RUSSIAN COLONISTS

Data as to the extent and value of the trade with Novaya Zemlya are available only from 1890 to 1910 inclusive. The total products for twenty years, 1890–1909 inclusive, were : 767 white bears, 42,352 roubles ; 11,372 sea dogs, 6,837 roubles ; 3,572 deer, 5,530 roubles ; 738 foxes, 3,645 roubles ; animal fat and oil, 24,612 puds, 41,329 roubles ; goltza, no value given, 939 puds. Total proceeds to include 1910, 127,635 roubles. Dividing these receipts into three periods of seven years each, the average yearly values were, first period 3,784; second 5,206; last 9,240, an increase of the last over the first of 244 per cent.

The products of the land chase have increased enormously in later years. The years 1926–1927 was most successful, particularly in fox trapping. Fifteen hundred foxes were secured, which at the current price of forty roubles per pelt amounted to sixty thousand roubles.

No figures are had as to the product and value of the fisheries of either of the Novaya Zemlya seas — the Barents and Kara — but it is reported that they are very large. The port of Murmansk on Barents Sea is in the process of rivaling Kandalaska, where the tributary streams of the White Sea are phenomenally productive.

On this point the "Times Book of Russia", 1815, says, "The lakes of Northwest Russia give employment in their fisheries to tens of thousands of professional fishermen and farmers. . . . The lake fisheries yield approximately 80,000 tons a year, not counting those used for local food."

In Russia, although its resources in temperate regions are enormous, arctic products are deemed worthy of systematic development.

CHAPTER XVI

ARCTIC ASIA

OF all arctic regions, the greatest in area, the most important in future development and the richest in natural resources is Northern Asia, which spans the three thousand miles between the Kara Sea and Bering Strait. For nearly three centuries the utilization of its wealth has been confined to the limited trade relations of Russians with the native hunters and reindeer breeders. Other terrestrial sources have remained practically untouched. Even in this century the contributory power along material lines is far inferior in Arctic Asia than in any other polar country.

Such conditions are due, first to the inertia and inattention of the general government, secondly to the character of its dissimilar tribes — primitive folk, uneducated and unfamiliar with modern methods and appliances — and lastly to the lack of economical communication with the markets of the world.

EXPLORATIONS

Stirred by the voyages of the Dutch and English into Kara Sea, Russians bent their energies to outline the northern coast of Asia, and extend to Northern Siberia their trade relations with the natives, their sole object and inspiration. As early as 1627 the onward march of traders in search of sable and other valuable furs had invaded the Lena Valley. Between 1636 and 1639 Elise Busa explored rivers draining into the Arctic Ocean, and succeeded in reaching the delta of the Lena; the Olenek to the west and the Vana to the east. About 1640 by an overland journey Postnik discovered the river Indigirka. As early as 1644 Russian traders pushed yet farther to the east, and in the valley of the Kolyma the Cossack Stadukin erected a trading post, destined to be the center of Russian influence for the exaction of tributes from the tribes and the accumulation of land and sea furs. By this date the northern coast of Asia had been traversed, except the shore to the west of the Olenek River.

The aim of Peter the Great to complete his knowledge of Asia resulted in the great survey of 1733–1742. Selinof in 1738 by reindeer sledge traced the shores of the Gulf of Obi northward to White (Belyi) Island. This, with the voyages of Muravief (1735–1736), Malygin and Skuratof, practically determined the continental outlines between Archangel and the Yenisei, 47 degrees of longitude apart.

After the loss of his ship, Chariton Laptief reached winter quarters on the Chatanga, twelve men perishing on the winter journey of cold and exhaustion. In the spring of 1741 Laptief continued his work by land in order to reach the northernmost point of Asia, an exceedingly difficult task from its distance and high latitude, 77° 34′ N., over six degrees farther north than Boothia Felix, North America. Laptief's exploration of the Taimyr Peninsula ended the western voyages. His mate, Chelyuskin, by a long, dangerous journey from the Chatanga, reached the North Cape, properly named for him; the doubts cast on this discovery were dissipated by Nordenskiold. The attempt in 1735 to explore east of the delta of the Lena was a complete and disastrous failure, as Lassinius and fifty-three of his sixty-two men died of scurvy in their winter quarters. His successor, Dmitri Laptief, pursued the work with great energy and resolution. By a series of journeys under conditions of danger and suffering between 1737 and 1742, he followed the northern shores east of the Kolyma River to Cape Baranof, through 30 degrees of longitude. Eventually he marched overland to the valley of the Anadyr. Thus gradually, at the expense of life and suffering, the northern coasts of Arctic Asia came within the knowledge of man.

Scant information is available concerning explorations in the late seventeenth and the eighteenth centuries of the enormous areas of Arctic Asia, which remained unsurveyed and in most sections

[167]

uninhabited.   The practice of Russia looked rather to the exploitation of the various tribes in the way of tributes, which began with the Yakuts in 1631, the Buriats in 1643, and in the exaction of supplies nominally for official use.   However, the persistent Russian trader sought out and visited every region where furs could be obtained from the natives, invariably by barter.   The inhabitants were principally tribes owning large herds of reindeer, for whose sustenance a nomadic life was necessary. These traders made journeys by dog or deer sledges of great distances, involving hardships and time ; but business and not surveys engaged their energies. In consequence, large areas remained unmapped, and within the past decade of this century official efforts, under Syedoff and others, have made important discoveries.

Difficulties of travel have prevented local authorities from giving other than theoretical attention to districts under their control ; journeys of months over trails thousands of miles in length do not appeal to most men.

The Trans-Siberian Railway has done something to make Northwest Siberia accessible, although one of its most northerly stations, Krasnoyarsk, is some four hundred miles south of the arctic circle. This city, founded in 1648, has about eighty thousand inhabitants and is the capital of the Yeniseisk district ; it is one thousand five hundred miles from the mouth of the Yenisei, on which river it is situated. The telegraph line stops at Monastir-Turukhansk, sixty miles south of the arctic zone, the capital of the Turukhansk district.

COLONIZATION AND RESOURCES

Emigration is usually induced by hope of material prosperity, which means abundant resources in the new environment. For more than three centuries all efforts to Russianize Siberia had practically no results. Tobolsk was thus founded in 1590, and in 1673 an administrative center was established at Irkutsk, but Arctic Asia continued to be a land of primitive people. In the twentieth century, in order to relieve disturbed economical conditions in Russia, the policy of stimulating immigration to Siberia was adopted, and offers of transportation, land and wood were made to such colonists. The expenditures for such purpose rose from $500,000 the first year to $12,000,000 in 1909. However, Arctic Asia did not share in the results. The new colonists, exceeding annually more than half a million in several years, settled on the fertile lands near the railway. In fact Northern Siberia suffered a decline in its Russian inhabitants, which had begun earlier.

Doctor Nansen in his valuable volume, "Through Siberia", 1914, states that Turukhansk has descended from its standing as a city to that as a village. In 1824 there were forty-six Russian homesteads north of that village, of which only twenty-seven remained in 1863. This despite the attractions of furs, fish and gold. He illuminates the situation, under which the natives are gradually disappearing, by many definite statements. At Obdorsk an annual tax is levied on every adult Yurak of 10.5 roubles, about $5.50. In addition the government has seized most of the best fishing stations on the Yenisei and levies a rental on their use. In return for its local receipts, Russia furnishes "no education, no doctors, no priests, no schools, no roads and no communications."

The great resources of Arctic Asia are forests, furs, gold and reindeer-breeding. Their current contributions in a material way to the world are lamentably small, due primarily to lack of speedy and economical communication with the world at large, and secondly to demoralizing habits among the natives arising from contact with unscrupulous traders. Nansen states that the fisheries of the lower Yenisei in 1907 employed about 2,000 men, who with their 750 seines caught vast numbers of fish, of which 3,000 tons were exported; the benefits to the natives were meager in the extreme. The fisheries of the Lena and Kolyma are of only local value, as means of shipment are practically nil. The land mammals have been a source of considerable profit, but hunting has been overdone, and future results are surmised with alarm. While the areas of gold-bearing rocks are extensive, their remoteness from centers of transportation and

supplies do not promise large products in the immediate future. For data on these and other subjects
the fullest available information is to be found
in the "Handbook of Siberia and Arctic Russia",
by the Naval Intelligence Bureau of the British
Admiralty.

Those interested in the native tribes can find
much information in the two volumes of Miss
M. A. Czaplicka: "My Siberian Year", and
"Aboriginal Siberia", 1914.

Data are lacking as to the present activities in
Arctic Asia, but evidently renewed attention is
given to conditions in Northern Siberia. As
evidence it is only necessary to note the daily relations between the Soviet Government and the
world at large, by the meteorological reports.
They are sent forth by radio from the Russian
station at Dickson, Northern Siberia, situated in
73° 30′ N., 80° 23′ E. If efforts along material
lines languish to a certain extent, the scientific
contributions accord with the dominating spirit of
the twentieth century.

The future prosperity of Arctic Asia depends on
improved communications. When steam traffic
becomes regular to the Yenisei via Yugor Strait,
and to Indigirka or the Lena via Bering Strait, the
advantages that will then accrue to Siberia will be
shared to a limited extent by her northern provinces.
The great mineral resources of Northern Asia can
become profitable only with better transporta-

tion, and with assurances of a stable and enduring government.

The phenomenal lack of geographic knowledge as to Arctic Asia has been disclosed in 1927 by the return of S. Obruchev from his explorations in the northern watershed of the Indigirka. He there found a region as large as Germany which was entirely unknown. It was supposed to be a plain, similar to that west of the river, and to be practically uninhabited. He found the country to the east filled largely by mountains, there being nine latitudinal alpine chains, which extend about six hundred fifty miles in length, and rise to more than ten thousand feet. He found living in permanent settlements 2,500 Yakuts and 350 Tungus. Geologically he discovered vast post-Tertiary glaciation (*Geographical Journal*, Nov., 1927). Yet this region, between 130° and 160° E., and from 62° N. to the Siberian Ocean, has been known theoretically for nearly three centuries.

CHAPTER XVII

THE ISLANDS OF THE SIBERIAN SEA

BETWEEN Bering Strait and the Kara Sea, the continental shelf of the great Siberian Ocean is dotted with widely separated islands. Until the discovery of the Nicholas II Archipelago, renamed Lenin Land, the most important — owing to their stores of ivory — were the New Siberian Islands, situated to the northeast of the delta of the Lena. The most southerly of these islands had been occasionally seen by traders skirting the continental coast between the Lena and the Indigirka; it was never visited until 1770 and then by a Russian trader after whom it was named.

Liakhof's journey was inspired by the sight of a large herd of deer, coming south from the ice-covered sea. Following their tracks by dog sledge in April, 1770, he reached Liakhof Island in a day, and pushing on, finally turned back from Maloi Island, sixty miles from the continent. Granted exclusive right of exploiting the land he had discovered, he visited the islands by boat in 1773 and wintering on Liakhof discovered Kotelnoi, where he found mammoth tusks. Lerchon's discovery of mammoth bones on the Siberian tundra, in this region, initiated a novel and profitable industry which extended to the New Siberian group. The scientific and material importance of these deposits led the Russian Government to send Chvoinof to survey the islands and make such researches as would solve the problem of existing conditions. He reported that except for a few granitic hills Liakhof was a mixture of ice, sand and ivory, the last element being the remains of the mammoth, fossil ox, rhinoceros and other extinct animals. Another unusual condition was the existence of moss beds of considerable thickness, underlain by permanent ice. Driftwood was abundant, ivory plentiful, fur-bearing animals numerous. From a mountain peak on Kotelnoi he saw in May a mountainous land to the north, doubtless the De Long Islands. At the commencement of the nineteenth century other islands were added to the archipelago, discovered by hunters — Stolbovoi and Fadajef (Thaddeus) by Samkif in 1805; Nova Sibir by Sirovatskof in 1806 and Bjeflkof by a hunter of that name in 1808.

To a fortunate complication regarding hunting rights were due the descriptions of Hedenstrom, so important to scientists. Sent by Chancellor Nicholas Romanzof to survey the islands, Hedenstrom with Sannikof and Koshevin as assistants, traveling by sledge in March, 1809, reached Thaddeus via Liakhof; his assistants surveyed this island while he continued on to Nova Sibir.

[174]

In 1809 with Sannikof he again visited the archipelago, reaching Nova Sibir with twenty-nine sledges, on March 13. On this island was found an axe made from a mammoth tusk, and on Thaddeus a Yukaghir sledge and skinning knife, evidences of its habitation at some remote period, before iron was obtainable by the Yukaghirs, who in 1914 to the number of 754 were yet living between the lower Yana and lower Kolyma rivers.

On the south coast of Nova Sibir were found the remarkable Wood Hills, two hundred feet high, consisting of alternate strata of sandstone and bituminous remains of trees. The wood was black, glossy, friable and in places seemed to be fossilized charcoal. Hedenstrom verified the almost incredible statement of Liakhof that the entire soil of Liakhof Island appeared to consist of mammoth bones. In any event the large cargoes of such bones, brought annually from the island, for nearly fifty years had not sensibly diminished the visible supply.

In 1810 Hedenstrom from his base on the Indigirka visited Nova Sibir, from which he sought to reach the De Long Islands. After travel for four days, open water was met, which caused his failure. Conditions became desperate, and food failing, they would have perished had they not killed ten polar bears; forty-three days of difficult travel brought them to land. Meanwhile Sannikof confined his researches to Kotelnoi, where, passing the summer with fur and mammoth hunters, he found in great quantities bones of the mammoth and other animals. Surveying the west coast, he was surprised to find the cross-marked grave of a Russian hunter, a partly furnished wooden house and the remains of a wrecked vessel. It appeared probable that some Archangel hunters had, by stress of weather and ice drift, involuntarily made the first voyage around Cape Chelyuskin, and sealed their discoveries with their lives. Surveys in 1811 by Sannikof and Pschenizyn had no important results, but from Thaddeus Island Sannikof saw an island, possibly Bennett, which he could not reach, owing to open water.

The journeys made by F. von Wrangel and P. F. Anjou, 1820–1823, on the Siberian Sea are of intense interest to any reader, but their material outcome was scanty. Under the most daring and dangerous exertions, under adverse conditions of ice, they failed to discover land to the east, west and north of the archipelago. The farthest point reached in 1823, by Anjou, was in 76° 36' N., 138° E., north of Kotelnoi, where the sea was only seventeen fathoms deep ; the reported land of Sannikof was not seen. Wrangel thoroughly explored Bear Islands, but his efforts to locate the land which Andrejev claimed to have seen in 1763 were failures, as indeed have been those of his successors (Sabine : "Wrangel's Polar Sea." 1844).

Wrangel's efforts ended Russian attempts to

explore the Siberian Sea and its geographical features became theoretical. Petermann, the great geographer, advanced an opinion that Wrangel Land was in the nature of an arctic continent, extending from the neighborhood of Asia across the Pole to Greenland. Even as late as 1881, Nordenskiold thought it possible that this land might connect with the archipelago to the north of America. The American De Long solved this problem at the expense of his life.

In 1879, Commander G. W. De Long, in the *Jeannette*, entered the pack in 71° 35' N., 175° W., expecting to winter on the shores of Wrangel Land, which he thought to be continental. Drifting nearly two years with the ice pack of the Siberian Ocean, the *Jeannette* was finally crushed and sank, July 2, 1881, in 77° 36' N., 155° E. Melville meanwhile had landed on a new island, Jeannette, barren, rocky and ice-capped. Later Henrietta Island was discovered in 77° 08' N., 158° E.

His ship sunk, De Long with five boats, nine sledges and provisions for sixty days, started for the New Siberian Islands, one hundred fifty miles distant. Adverse drift carried them to 77° 36' N., 155° E., an unprecedented latitude in this ocean. Later they fortunately discovered and landed on Bennett Island, where they rested nine days. On this island, in 76° 38' N., 148° E., they explored seventeen miles of the southern coast, and found great numbers of birds, which enabled them to re-

plenish their waning supply of food.   Starting south
they landed, August 19, on Thaddeus Island, one of
the New Siberian group.   The sea being open, they
sailed to the Lena delta, where on September 12,
1882, they encountered a violent storm, in which
Chipp's boat with eight men foundered, and all
perished.   The boats of De Long and Melville
were then separated.   Entering an eastern mouth
of the Lena, Melville with his nine men reached,
on September 26, Geeomovialocke, a Russian
village.

De Long and Doctor Ambler, with twelve men,
landed on September 17, in 73° 25′ N., 126° 30′ E.,
but the water was so shallow that they had to
abandon their boat.   Unfortunately their passage
inland was prevented by deep and unfordable
tributaries, obliging them to defer crossing until
ice formed.   Finally when they reached the shore
of the Lena, men fell sick and could not march,
while food failed and game was absent.   Under
these conditions, with one man dead, the two
strongest seamen were sent forward to obtain relief ;
they reached Belun on October 29, quite exhausted.
De Long and Ambler remained with the dying men,
and finally all perished of starvation.   Melville's
efforts to relieve his comrades failed, but he discovered their bodies on March 23, 1882.   Apart
from valuable physical observations in an unknown
region, the geographic results of the De Long expedition were extensive and enlightening.   Nearly

fifty thousand square miles of the Arctic Ocean were visited, and the general character of as much more disclosed. It proved that the continental shelf of Northern Siberia extends far northward, and that it is dotted by numerous small islands.

The Imperial Russian Geographical Society in 1885 did exploratory work under Bunge and Von Toll. While making collections in Jana Land they found in April, 1886, at Bor-Urgag, on the Dodomo, the skeleton of a mammoth covered with moss and other vegetation. Making the New Siberian Islands his base of research, Von Toll left Great Liakhof to Bunge, and devoted his efforts mainly to Kotelnoi — though he made side visits to adjacent islands. He traversed the entire coasts of Kotelnoi and labored under the impression that he saw the land of Sannikof, 1811. Bunge was unusually successful in his researches on Great Liakhof, where the upper layers of clay furnished fossils in great quantities and variety. Among these were remains of the mammoth, musk ox and rhinoceros, with bones of deer, horses and two new species of the ox.

Toll states that the mammoths were always found in masses of clay, pressed into broad fissures of the underlying ground ice. The destruction of the rich fauna at the edge of the ice masses of the glacial period is attributed to the gradual sinking of the coasts, which restricted the land area that furnished nutrition. These researches enriched knowledge in botany, geology and paleontology.

In 1893 Toll sought mammoth remains on the east of Jana Land. Later with Shileiko he reached by dog sledge 75° 37′ N., on the west coast of Kotelnoi. While making physical observations and rich collections, Toll found evidence that in the mammoth age trees grew in 74° N., fully three degrees of latitude beyond their present limit. On Great Liakhof he discovered frozen carcasses of rhinoceros and musk oxen, with remains of ante-lopes, American stags, mammoth and even a tiger. In the remarkable wood mountain, among other species there was an entire tree (*Alnus fruticosa*) ninety feet long, with fruit, leaves and roots.

To perfect his geological knowledge, especially as to the Tertiary deposits on Bennett and adjacent islands, Toll made his fatal expedition in the *Zarya*. Wintering, 1900–1901, in 76° 08′ N., 95° E., he explored the Nordenskiold Islands, and part of the North Taimyr Peninsula. In the summer of 1901 his efforts to reach Bennett Island and to attain the legendary Sannikof Land were unsuccessful. The *Zarya* was frozen in and wintered at Nerpichi Bay, Kotelnoi, 1901–1902. On June 7, 1902, with astronomer Seeberg and two hunters, Toll left for Bennett Island, which was reached on August 3, 1902 ; the island is in general a plateau, with no high land exceeding one thousand five hundred feet. Arctic animals were present — bears, reindeer and walrus. Geological researches disclosed the presence of Cambrian deposits, bones of mammoth and other animals of the Quaternary period. The party started back to Kotelnoi on November 8, and doubtless perished en route. The relief expeditions of Brusneff and Kolchak in 1904 found a record of the above discoveries, cached on Bennett Island, but no traces of the men were found on any of the New Siberian group.

Toll's contributions have a most important influence in determining the areas and types of deposits of the Tertiary period in Arctic Siberia. Connected therewith are the problems of shifting geographical poles and climatic changes since the end of the Tertiary period. The value of the researches of Von Toll in Siberia has been enhanced by Maddren's discoveries in Alaska of Pleistocene mammals. (Bunge & Toll: "Expedition nach Neusiberien Insen", 1887; Toll, "Russian Polar Expedition." *Geographical Journal*, 1902).

The greatest interest attaches to Wrangel Land, for which in 1824 Wrangel looked in vain from Baranof Rock. Fog prevented John Rodgers from seeing it in 1849, when he sailed within a few miles of it. On August 14–16, 1867, Thomas Long, in the American whaler *Niles*, discovered it and sailed along its southern shore. Bliven, Philips and Raynor visited it the same year, as did Stockton in 1889.

An effort to make Wrangel Land contributory

[181]

to the material welfare of the world, by occupation and exploitation, was made by V. Stefansson. Through him a colony was thereon established (Stefansson : "The Adventure of Wrangel Land"). However, the Soviet Government protested against the occupation as a violation of Russian territory. Ejecting the colonists on the island, a new settlement was established, consisting of a large number of Siberian natives, under control of three Soviet officials. It is expected that the colony will be able to live on the land and sea game of the region. Annual visits by airplane are planned.

The most extensive additions to the geography of the Siberian Sea, since the discovery of the New Siberian Islands, have been the contributions made under Vilkitski during his expeditions of 1910–1915. While the hydrographic work was very important, the most notable result was the discovery of Nicholas II Archipelago (renamed Lenin), about half a dozen islands lying some fifty miles to the north of Cape Chelyuskin. Discovered in 1913, they were again visited in 1914, and a landing made. The southwestern cape of the main island is in 77° 50′ N., 99° E. From that point the southern and eastern shores were traced to 80° 04′ N., 97° 12′ W., by observation and to 81° N., by dead reckoning; the northern limit could not be reached on account of ice. That these islands have not been discovered by the many explorers who have

passed near was due to the difficulty of distinguish-
ing snow-covered land from the ice floes which
cover the sea. Detailed accounts of these discoveries are given by Transehe, "The Siberian
Sea Road", "Russian Expeditions", 1910–1915
(*Geographical Review*, XV, 1925).

CHAPTER XVIII

ARCTIC AVIATION

ACTIVE efforts to explore the polar regions by air travel began with S. A. Andrée, who had been a member of the Swedish International Polar Expedition of 1882. An aëronaut of some experience, he established his base at Danes Island, Spitsbergen, in 1896. Adverse winds and an unsuitable balloon — which was quite permeable — forecast disaster and prevented an attempt that year.

With an improved balloon a start was made on July 11, 1897; the balloon carried a load of about five tons — food, men, freight and ballast. Accompanying Andrée were Strindberg and Fraenkel. Three message buoys, dropped by Andrée, have been found, from which it is known that the balloon had reached 83° N., 25° E. The balloon was then at an altitude of 820 feet, over a rugged ice field, and was moving not north, but 45 degrees east of north. Repeated searches have failed to disclose under what conditions the party perished (Stadling: "Andrée's Flight into the Unknown." *Century Magazine*, Nov., 1897).

Wellman's attempt to utilize a balloon in his Spitsbergen explorations was equally unsuccessful, but was unmarked by disaster. In July, 1923, a German aviator planned explorations in Spitsbergen, where he established a base at Green Harbor. He made a number of successful short flights by seaplane — up Ice Fiord, across New Friesland, along the north coast to Danes Island, and elsewhere. He did not venture over the Arctic Ocean.

Coincident with the round-the-world flight between April 6 and September, 1924, arctic aviation was again attempted. In renewing the arctic explorations of the Oxford University, George Binney resolved to use a seaplane. The seaplane *Athene*, dismounted and crated, was carried to Green Harbor. It proved to be an inferior machine, and after it was assembled many defects were discovered before it was put to use. Finally Binney and a companion started on a flight from Green Harbor to Leifde Bay, on the north coast. Half the journey was made, when the engine stalled and the plane fell into the middle of Foreland Sound. The seaplane drifted toward the open sea, and the party only escaped death by the help of three Norwegians in a motor boat, who happened to see them.

Thereafter one trouble after another developed. The seaplane was taken to Leifde Bay and repaired, and after short use was again disabled. Brought into serviceable condition anew, it flew to Treurenberg Bay; it once more was disabled. Finally

[185]

repaired, it did notable survey work over Northeast Land, and was eventually wrecked and abandoned. Fortunately, with all these troubles no one was injured (Binney: "With Seaplane and Sledge in the Arctic." 1927).

Although the experiences of Amundsen and Ellsworth disclosed the dangers of long journeys in the arctic with a plane, yet R. E. Byrd and F. Bennett ventured their lives in a north-polar voyage. The plane used was a Fokker, equipped with three Wright-Whirlwind engines. Establishing their base at Kings Bay, Spitsbergen, they started north at 12.30 A.M., May 9, 1926, and reached the North Pole at 9.04 A.M. The return flight was made with the same rapidity, and at about 3.30 P.M. they were back at Kings Bay. The flight was accomplished in fifteen and a half hours, without trouble of any serious character.

Byrd's initiation was at Etah, with the Mac-Millan expedition of 1925. While he then failed to reach unknown land, owing to bad weather, extended flights gave him confidence in polar aviation. His present expedition looks to an aërial survey of the continent of Antarctica.

Most notable are the arctic flights which marked the final career of Amundsen as an explorer. The earliest extended air journey in the arctic rëgions was that of Amundsen and Ellsworth, made from Spitsbergen in 1925. They left Kings Bay on May 21 in two Dornier flying boats, carrying fuel for one thousand two hundred miles and food for twenty days. One boat was occupied by Amundsen, Riiser-Larsen and Feucht, the other by Ellsworth, Dietrichson and Omdal.

The flight was made to 87° 43′, when engine trouble obliged them to land. The open lead in which the machine rested froze solid that day. At this place two soundings were made, which indicated that the ocean had a depth of about twelve thousand feet. As one boat was now disabled, they were obliged to return in the other. To launch it a level runway had to be constructed, which was accomplished by twenty-five days of continuous and exhausting labor. On June 15 they took the air and reached open water and Spitsbergen in safety.

A most spectacular and perilous arctic flight was made in the *Norge*, an Italian dirigible plane, from Spitsbergen to Alaska in 1926. In this historic voyage were sixteen persons: Amundsen, Ellsworth, Nobile the pilot, Riiser-Larsen, Horgen, Wisting, Gottwaldt, Malmgren, Ondal, Ramm, Storm-Johnsen, and five Italian mechanics.

The *Norge* left Kings Bay, Spitsbergen, 9.05 A.M. (all times Greenwich), May 11, 1926, and reached the North Pole at 1.25 A.M., May 12. No land or water was seen en route, and the only visible life were two polar bears. There were dropped an American, a Norwegian and an Italian flag on the north-polar floes. The ice was much broken up,

[187]

with piles of small floes. The aviators were troubled by great masses of fog after passing the Pole. At 8.45 A.M., May 13, land was seen, probably Point Barrow. Owing to bad weather, they could not select a place to descend until 7 A.M., May 14, when the *Norge* landed safely at Teller, Alaska (Amundsen and Ellsworth: "First Crossing of the Polar Sea." 1927). The distance traversed was estimated at 3,300 miles, though Kings Bay and Teller are only 2,700 miles apart. Thus ended a historic epoch in aviation without disaster of any kind.

The most notable and dangerous arctic flights are those made over the Beaufort Sea region by George Wilkins and Carl B. Eielson. In April, 1926, they left Point Barrow in a Fokker single-engine plane and flew north about one hundred forty miles, penetrating a considerable distance into the unknown regions. No land was seen.

Renewing their explorations in 1927, Wilkins and Eielson left Point Barrow on March 29, in a Stinson plane, with fuel for one thousand four hundred miles in good weather. They flew to the northwest five hundred fifty miles, when engine trouble developed and they had to make a forced landing. Here they made two sonic soundings, and found the ocean to be about three miles deep. Temporary repairs were made and they turned towards Barrow. But it was no avail, and after dark they were forced down into rough ice, which disabled their plane beyond repair. Making sledges from the woodwork of the plane, they started for shore. Five days' drift on the floes of Beaufort Sea and final travel with packs brought them to land at Eskimo Point.

Their escape was almost miraculous, but Eielson lost a finger by frost (Byrd and Stefansson: *Science*, May 27, 1927). No land was seen.

Armitage, of the Scott Expedition, also made a balloon ascent in the Antarctic (Chapter XXIII).

CHAPTER XIX

NORTH-POLAR VOYAGES

CONTRARY to the general impression, arctic voyages for the attainment of the North Pole have been the exception rather than the rule. Robert Thorne successfully urged on Henry the Eighth a renewal of the search for a short route to China by sailing across the Arctic Ocean; of the resulting voyage of two ships in 1527, only their failure is definitely known.

The first recorded voyage of Henry Hudson, May 1, 1607, was to discover a passage by the North Pole to China and Japan. Although the main intent failed, far-reaching results followed in the development of the whale fisheries of Spitsbergen. The voyage of Jonas Poole, 1610–1611, turned to a fishing venture in the Greenland Sea.

In June, 1773, the attempt was renewed under Captain J. C. Phipps, afterwards Lord Mulgrave, in the *Racehorse*, supported by Captain S. Lutwidge in the *Carcass*. They followed the edge of the ice barrier off the west coast of Spitsbergen to the northwest beyond the 80th parallel, when further progress was impossible. Eventually Phipps abandoned the attempt, after reaching 80° 48′ N.,

20° E., a higher latitude than that attained by his predecessors. Especial interest attaches to this expedition as the immortal Nelson, then a lad of fifteen, served as Phipps' coxswain. The lad displayed his courage by attacking a polar bear under most dangerous circumstances.

In 1817, Great Britain sent forth a squadron to reach the Pacific by sailing across the Arctic Ocean. The *Dorothea*, commanded by Captain D. Buchan, was supported by the *Trent* under Lt. John Franklin, just recovering from his wound received in the battle of New Orleans. Rendezvousing in Magdalena Bay, Spitsbergen, the ships were ice-beset in 80° 37′ N. While a violent storm freed the vessels, the *Dorothea* was so badly crushed by ice pressures that the squadron returned to England.

Whalers were not interested in reaching the Pole, but doubtless some of the Dutch skippers, hundreds of whom annually reached the 80th parallel, found open water to the north with a favorable wind that would have carried them several degrees beyond. Exact data are wanting as to their northings, but tales of sailing to the Pole may well be discredited. However, William Scoresby, the famous English whaler, passed far beyond any other authenticated northing when, May 24, 1806, he reached 81° 30′ N., 19° E. (Scoresby: "Polar Regions." 1823).

Holding fast to the Spitsbergen route for the Pole, as the most promising of navigable seas,

William Parry followed it in 1827. Profiting by his four previous arctic voyages, he outfitted his expedition most carefully. The *Hecla* once safe in Trurenberg Bay, Parry decided, owing to ice conditions, to make his attempt by boat, so he left behind tame reindeer brought as draught animals for sledging.

On June 23, Parry left Little Table, Seven Islands, with twenty-eight souls provisioned for seventy-one days. His two boats were fitted with steel-shod runners, to facilitate their use as sledges over extended ice floes.

Continued bad weather, small detached floes, frequent but disconnected water pools hampered Parry's progress. Changes of the boats to and from the sea were necessary several times each march. Frequently the ice was so rough that the cargoes were advanced in parts, so that often the same floe was traversed five times. The pointed ice made floe travel difficult, as the ice cut both boots and feet.

Making a northing of about ten miles a day, the distance decreased steadily. Parry finally learned that the main pack was drifting rapidly south, and that the attempt must be abandoned. The extreme point reached, 82° 45' N., 20° E., was 172 miles from the *Hecla*. The entire distance traveled was 970 miles in sixty-one days. The expedition failed to win the £1,000 offered if it reached 83° N., but it secured for England a new record of the highest latitude, which for forty-eight years was unbeaten.

The voyages of Kane, 1853, and Hayes, 1860 (Chapter VIII), were not openly north-polar, though incidentally such was the intent.

The primary effort of Sweden was initiated in 1868, by Nordenskiold, who sailed in the *Sofia* as scientific chief, with Von Otter in command. From the base in Smeerenberg Harbor, Von Otter succeeded in reaching, on September 19, 81° 42′ N., 17° 30′ E. This was the highest latitude then attained by ship, though it has since often been surpassed. Injury by ice to the *Sofia* compelled abandonment of the voyage. Nordenskiold organized another expedition in 1872, looking to sledge travel by reindeer. Under Palander the *Polhem* established winter quarters in Mussel Bay. Leaving with three sledges, Nordenskiold met such rough ice that he reached Phipps Island with but a single sled left. Discouraged, he returned to the ship by the way of the inland ice of Northeast Land.

The first German north-polar expedition was commanded by Koldewey, in the *Germania*, in 1868. Ice conditions prevented the *Germania* from reaching East Greenland, so Koldewey returned home after attaining 81° 05′ north of Spitsbergen. The second expedition, 1869–1870, under Koldewey in the *Germania*, supported by Hagemann in the *Hansa*, planned to sail north

[193]

along the east coast of Greenland. The *Germania* reached East Greenland, where it made important local discoveries (Chapter X) but failed in its polar quest. The *Hansa* was beset and frozen in; carried south by drift, she was crushed on October 19. The crew built a house on the floe, with which they drifted over six hundred miles southward, along and in sight of the barren shores of Greenland. On May 7, 1870, after a drift of two hundred and one days, they launched their boats in 61° 12′ N., and rounding Cape Farewell reached Friedrichstal on June 13, 1870.

The only north-polar expedition sent forth by the United States was that of the *Polaris*, under Charles Francis Hall; its fortunes are set forth in Chapter VIII. Hall carried his ship to 82° 11′ N., thus surpassing Von Otter, 1868, while one of Hall's crew, Myer, made the land record in 82° 07′ N.

The voyage of the British polar expedition is also recorded in Chapter VIII. It made a world's northing, when A. H. Markham on May 12, 1876, reached 83° 20′ N., 64° W., on the Great Frozen Sea. Supported as far as Cape Henry, 82° 55′ N., Markham entered the hummocks on April 10, with two sledges and seventeen men. Starting with two boats, he soon abandoned one but the other was hauled to the end. Unfortunately the sledgemen were attacked by scurvy; five broke down completely and had to be hauled on the sledges after the abandonment of the second boat. Other men became unable to pull the sledges, and the whole party was in danger of perishing. They were saved through the extraordinary march of twenty-four hours made by A. C. Parr, who obtained a relief party from the *Alert*, at Floeberg Beach. One sledgeman died en route, and eleven others of the original seventeen were hauled to the ship on sleds.

The geographic successes of the so-called Greely expedition are related in Chapter VIII. The north-polar success was due to J. B. Lockwood and D. L. Brainard; they had proved their fitness by a preliminary journey to Greenland, from Lady Franklin Bay, made in temperatures averaging 74 degrees below freezing for ten days, — a period of intense prolonged cold never experienced by any field party, either before or since. This extreme test gave confidence, as no man suffered injury, not even the weakest, — no Arctic team is stronger or more enduring than its feeblest member.

Lockwood left Lady Franklin Bay April 3, 1882, under orders "to explore the coast of Greenland near Cape Britannia", which was thought to be separated from Greenland, and beyond that point to proceed "in such direction as he thought best to carry out the objects of the (main) expedition, — the extension of knowledge regarding lands within the arctic circle." The advance party was supported as far as Cape Bryant under violent blizzards and during intense cold, which touched 81 degrees below freezing.

With Brainard, Eskimo Christiansen, one dog-sled and rations for twenty-five days, Lockwood left Cape Bryant and traveled across the frozen sea direct to Cape Britannia, which was reached in six marches. En route they made a sounding where no bottom was found in one hundred thirty-seven fathoms, — indicating their passage beyond the continental shelf. From the highest point at Cape Britannia, 2,050 feet, Victoria Inlet was seen as "an immense fiord running to the south; no land visible at the head; all to the south is an indistinct mass of snow-covered mountains, ending in about 82° 30′ N."

Having reached land never before traveled by civilized man, they rounded Cape Frederick, crossed Nordenskiold, Chipp and Mascart Inlets, and camped May 7 at Low Point 83° 07′, in equal latitude with the most northerly known land. Beyond Cape Ramsay the land ran east, and in twelve miles they lost two miles of latitude. Then came De Long Fiord, one of the immense inlets along the coast that showed no signs of heading. On May 10 at 83° 19′ N., 42° 21′ W., a violent gale entombed them sixty-three hours, during which they tasted food only at intervals of fifteen, twenty-four and nineteen hours, so as to extend their discoveries. Now floes were so high that the sledge was lowered and raised by dog traces; ice became so rough that the road was axe-cleared, and wide water cracks increased along the ice foot, and impeded progress. Despite all obstacles they reached, May 13, 1882, Lockwood Island, 83° 24' N., 42° 45' W., by astronomical observations. It was the farthest point of their sledge journey, in the most northerly latitude then attained by man.

From a cliff 2,600 feet high, their view north extended beyond the 84th parallel, "an unbroken expanse of ice, unbroken to the horizon" within 360 miles of the Pole. To the northeast they saw Cape Washington, about 83° 35' N., 38° W., with a faint possibility of northward-extending coast to the east of Washington, probably near Cape Jessup. To the south was "a confused mass of snow-capped peaks, the country much broken by entering fiords", unfavorable to any extended ice cap (Greely: "Three Years of Arctic Service." 1886).

The expedition of De Long, in 1879 via Bering Strait, is treated in Chapter XVII. His ship, the *Jeannette*, reached the most northerly latitude to date in the Siberian Ocean, 77° 36', 155° E.

Expeditions via Franz Josef Land (Chapter XIV) have been unsuccessful save that of Abruzzi. Payer, in 1874, reached Cape Fligely, 81° 51' N.; Wellman, 1894, attained 81° N.; Jackson, 1894, reached 81° 20' N.; the most northern point attained by the Ziegler expeditions of 1901 and

1904 (Baldwin, Fiala and Peters) was by the ship *America*, 82° 04′ N., then a record for a vessel.

The only very high latitude by this route is that attained by the expedition of Prince Luigi Amadeo, Duke of the Abruzzi, in the *Stella Polare*, 1900–1901. From the anchorage in Teplitz Bay, 82° 04′ N., Cagni started March 11, 1901, with twelve sledges, ten men and ninety-eight dogs. There were two supporting parties; the first, consisting of Querini and two seamen, turned shipward March 23, and were never seen again; the second, under Cavalli, reached Teplitz Bay safely. Cagni reached on April 25, 1901, 86° 34′ N., 65° 20′ E. To the north there was no land visible, only an unbroken expanse of rough ice. The magnetic variation was zero. Cagni surpassed the northing of Nansen by twenty-two miles, and the honor of the farthest north passed to Italy. Cagni's return journey covered sixty days, against forty-five days outward. The steady southwest drift of the polar pack made the situation hazardous, and despite every effort the party was carried by May 12 to longitude 48° 40′ E. After nine days' travel to the southeast they were on the same meridian. By almost incredible exertions during travel for four weeks, they barely reached, on June 13, Harley Island, the farthest westerly on the parallel, and thus escaped death (Abruzzi: "On the Polar Star." 2 vols. 1903).

The most daring attempt to reach the Pole was

that of S. A. Andrée, by a free balloon. He left
Danes Island on June 11, 1897, with two companions. The last message from Andrée was 10 P.M.
the same day, when the balloon was in 82° N.,
25° E., and moving N.N.E. Repeated search
has had no results.

Doctor F. Nansen, distinguished by his crossing
of the inland ice of Greenland (Chapter IX), initiated in 1893 a novel and dangerous north-polar
voyage. Ignoring the accepted canons of ice
navigation of avoiding besetment and seeking the
protected lee of land masses, he planned a repeti-
tion of the *Jeannette* drift (Chapter XVII) by
placing his vessel in the great ice pack near the
New Siberian Islands. Basing his success on
scientific data, such as the Siberian diatoms on
the coast of Greenland, he anticipated that his
ship would drift across the Pole. With a specially
constructed vessel, the *Fram*, navigated by Sverdrup, he entered the Siberian Ocean, via Kara Sea.
An unusually open sea favored his progress, and
the *Fram* was frozen in northwest of the New
Siberian Islands in 78° 50′ N., 134° E. on September
25, 1893. The ice pack moved largely through the
impulse of winds, and was generally unbroken,
though in January, 1895, destruction of the ship
was threatened by violent movements of the ice.

The *Fram* was beset thirty-five months, during
which period no land rose out of the surrounding
desolate polar expanse; only a few arctic birds

and an occasional animal relieved the monotony of snow and ice. The drift track was occasionally zigzag, but in the main it trended to the west-northwest to its highest latitude, 85° 57′ N., in longitude 60° E. Changing to a south-southwestern direction, the ship was carried to 84° 09′ N., 15° E., where she remained almost stationary from February to June, 1896. By skillful ice navigation Sverdrup brought the *Fram* into the open sea August 13, 1896, after a world record for his ship.

Nansen was not satisfied with the ship's northing, and when she was still beset in 84° 04′ N., 102° E., with Johansen as a companion, he decided to attempt to reach the Pole and return via Franz Josef Land. The extreme hazard of such a journey can be fully realized only by men of Arctic experience; its perils were obvious to these brave men whose perilous experiences made their journey one of the most extraordinary in polar annals.

They started with three sledges, twenty-eight dogs, two kayaks; the men provisioned for one hundred days, the dogs for thirty days. Nansen expected that they would reach the Pole in fifty days, but ice conditions were so bad that in twenty-three days he only reached 86° 12′ N., 100° E., one hundred twenty-eight miles of latitude from the *Fram*, with the Pole yet two hundred twenty-eight miles distant on April 7, 1895. He wisely determined to turn southward, faced with the probability of a march of five months to reach land.

Violent gales, dense fogs and a disintegrating pack seriously retarded travel. Food gradually failed, and the weakest dogs were killed and fed to the team, until two only remained. The men were in dire straits when Johansen fortunately shot a seal. Nansen was disabled for two days by rheumatism, which, if long prolonged, would have cost their lives. Johansen narrowly escaped death, when struck down on the march by a polar bear. Their watches ran down, so their observations for longitude were unreliable ; and land was not yet visible. Finally Eva Island was seen, and by alternate use of sledge and kayak they reached land on August 14, 1895. Conditions were unfavorable for Nansen's plan of reaching Spitsbergen, so they selected a suitable location on Franz Josef Land, where they built a stone hut for winter quarters. Polar bears were so numerous as not only to furnish abundant food, but also to be a menace to safety.

Starting May 19, 1896, for Spitsbergen, matters went badly. Nansen barely escaped drowning by falling into the sea through a soft floe. June 12 their kayak drifted away, and was only recovered by almost superhuman efforts of Nansen, swimming in the icy ocean. Two days later their meat was entirely gone, and a walrus injured the kayak. Their chances of survival were almost gone, when on June 17 they met near Cape Flora, Jackson, who was exploring the archipelago. Though Nansen had failed to reach the Pole, he had made a world record of arctic latitude.

By a series of voyages and sledge journeys, unapproached in polar exploration, Robert E. Peary applied his assiduous and remarkable energy to the attainment of the North Pole. He adopted the standard method of sledge journeys from a permanent land base, established by a specially fitted supporting ship. Explorations subsidiary to the polar quest are recorded in Chapter VIII.

His earliest strictly north-polar journeys were made during his expedition of 1898–1902, via Smith Sound. Unable in 1898 to force the *Windward* into Kennedy Channel, he was obliged to winter at Cape D'Urville. Planning to make Fort Conger (Greely's quarters, 1881–1883), he unwisely made a sledge journey to that point in December. Had it not been for the quarters and supplies at Conger he would have perished; as it was he passed weeks there unable to travel, for his feet were so badly frozen that he lost eight toes, amputated after his return to the *Windward*, March 13.

His ship returning to the United States, Peary remained at Etah, where he organized his Eskimo allies. In 1900 he decided to try the Greenland route (Chapter VIII), but only reached latitude 83° 35′ N.

Finding the eastern route impracticable, he established his winter quarters (1900–1901) at Fort Conger, and the following spring attempted the Hecla route. He failed even to reach the Arctic Ocean, and turned back at Lincoln Bay. He then moved his base southward to Payer Harbor, where six of his Eskimos died.

Undismayed, Peary renewed the attempt in 1902, and starting north reached Fort Conger by twelve wonderful marches. Leaving that station February 24, he reached the Arctic Ocean with nine sledges. Entering the ice April 8, with seven men and six sledges, he found travel arduous and slow, due to the shifting, disintegrating pack, whose constant shiftings furnished alternations of rubble, open water and young ice. Strong gales kept the party storm-bound, and often disrupted even the heaviest floes ; one lead was closed with such violence that it formed a pressure ridge about ninety feet high. At his farthest point, observations gave 84° 17′ N., 70° W., with a magnetic variation of 99 degrees west.

With a persistence unsurpassed in arctic annals, Peary renewed his polar quest in 1905. Sailing in the *Roosevelt*, he wintered on the northeastern coast of Grant Land. With an equipment never before equalled, and aided by a large force of Eskimos and their dogs, success seemed assured. Ice conditions, however, were so unfavorable that he was forced to turn back in 87° 06′ N., 70° W.

Though he had failed to reach the North Pole, he made a world record of arctic latitude.

Peary's final voyage was made in the *Roosevelt*, built for polar service under his supervision. The Peary Arctic Club equipped the expedition with munificence; his associates were collegians, enthusiastic in work of exploration and research; years of comradeship with the Etah natives ensured his mainstay in field work, with their sledges and dogs. The *Roosevelt* left Etah on August 18, 1908, with its equipage increased by forty-nine Eskimos and two hundred twenty-six dogs; she wintered at Cape Sheridan on the exposed shores of the paleocrystic sea. Working until November 5, field parties established as far as Cape Columbia, 83° 07' N., depôts of supplies needful for spring sledging.

February 15, 1909, the journey towards the Pole began. Peary left Cape Columbia on March 1, with a force of twenty-four men, nineteen sledges and one hundred thirty-three dogs. The order of the march was in two divisions: lightly equipped pioneers, with Bartlett, Hansen and Marvin alternately in charge, preceded Peary's division by a day and cleared the trail for its advance.

The past winter had been very severe, and the temperature of 52 degrees below freezing now prevailed. It was expected that the Arctic Ocean would present an unbroken expanse of heavy ice. Instead of such conditions, however, the reverse obtained. Peary explains that they resulted from the combined action of the tides and currents, with consequent disruption of the main floes and vast upheavals of pressure ridges. Such breaks occur along the edge of the continental shelf, where its shallow waters are abruptly succeeded by great oceanic depths.

Four marches poleward, Peary was greatly concerned to fall in with adverse conditions; he found extended areas of open water of such form and distribution as threatened the success of his journey. Meanwhile the temperatures were exceedingly low, causing frostbites. The support under Goodsell turned back March 14, from 84° N. Then the continental shelf had been passed, as a sounding showed a depth of 325 fathoms, and the ice improved. Borup returned from 85° 23′ N., and Marvin followed from 86° 38′ N. Marvin was supposed to have perished by drowning, but it later developed that he was killed by one of the Eskimos, after discussion over methods of march. The last supporting sledge, under Bartlett, was sent back from 87° 48′ N.

Peary said of his five remaining men, Negro Hansen and four Eskimos: "My party, my equipments and my supplies (are) in shape beyond the expectation of my most sanguine years." In five forced marches he covered, exclusive of detours, 138 miles over ice of difficult character for sledging. He reported that the sea was covered with unbroken and rough ice, with no land in sight, when he claimed that he reached the North Pole on April 6, 1909. Peary's return to Cape Columbia, 485 miles in a straight line, was made in sixteen days, a record of rapid travel never equaled by any other explorers, and which surpassed his own experiences in many years of field work.

That Peary entered regions adjacent to the Pole is unquestioned by any arctic expert, and his claim of reaching the Pole has been accepted by some geographic societies. Others, among whom are his predecessors over the Great Frozen Sea, view with serious doubt his accuracy. The reasons advanced by them for their adverse judgment are as follows: character of ice, shown by Peary's photographs; condition of dogs, worn down by hard travel; unsurpassed rapidity of travel over rough sea ice for a distance that must have far exceeded — with a minimum of detours — 530 miles; that with tired dogs he far exceeded the return journey of his supporting parties with fresher teams; and his inaccuracies as to accomplishments earlier made (Chapter VIII). Fairness to uninformed readers requires that this statement be made.

Doctor Cook claimed to have reached the North Pole in 1906, a claim generally and properly discredited. However, it is beyond question that his field experiences in 1905–1906 were most remarkable, — rarely if ever equaled and never surpassed for their extent, duration and endurance, — equipment and conditions considered. Starting with a small amount of food, Cook, with two Eskimos, Etuki Shuk and Ahwelah, lived on the country for fourteen months, — one entire winter and part of another, about seven months being in total darkness. He crossed Grant Land and entered the ice of the Great Frozen Sea in latitude about 83° N. How far north he proceeded will never be known. He returned safely with his two natives, without food and in conditions of almost utter exhaustion. To have lived so long in the field north of the 80th parallel, where game is exceedingly scarce, is almost a miracle. It is the irony of fate that such an achievement should be marred by unfounded claims as to the latitude reached.

The attainment of the Pole by Byrd in 1925 and the transpolar voyage of Amundsen and Ellsworth the same year are recorded under Aviation, Chapter XVIII.

The Russian expeditions of Sedoff and Broussilov, 1912–1914, were disastrous. Sedoff reached Franz Josef Land, where he died; his expedition returned to Archangel. Broussilov's ship, *St. Anna*, was caught in the pack and drifted north in Kara Sea, 1,540 miles in eighteen months, and reached 82° 55′ N., about seventy miles north of Rudolph Land. The crew separated, some abandoning the ship; only two are known to have survived.

CHAPTER XX

THE INTERNATIONAL CIRCUMPOLAR
STATIONS

THE importance of scientific research in the polar regions has been more or less appreciated since the beginning of the 19th century. Only within the past fifty years have the natural sciences been regularly represented on polar voyages, and valuable as were the results they were restricted and inconclusive. A revolution was wrought in this respect through the efforts of Lieutenant Charles Weyprecht, Austrian Navy, which eventuated in the establishment of the International Circumpolar Stations.

His experiences in the *Tegetthof* (Chapter XIV) bore fruit in an address to the German Scientific and Medical Association, at Gratz in 1875. Demonstrating that extended polar explorations were essential to the elucidation of the laws of Nature, he urged that scientific methods should dominate future action. Scientific research should be the primary object, and geographic exploration should be pursued in such directions as would increase our knowledge in some branch of science. Subjects of study should be carried on in specially selected regions, and observations should be continuous, coöperative and simultaneous.

Prince Bismarck appointed a commission of eminent scientists, which reported that such re-

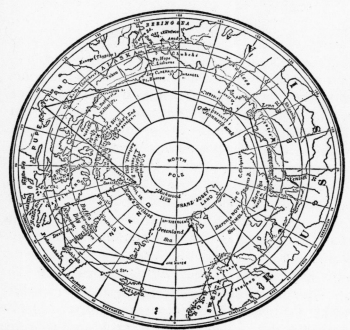

ARCTIC REGIONS, SHOWING LOCATION OF CIRCUMPOLAR
STATIONS, 1881–83

search would be most valuable, that success could only be obtained through the united action of several nations. The proposition was submitted to the Bundesrath, and other nations were invited to participate.

Weyprecht and Count Wilczek presented a plan to the International Meteorological Congress, which decided "that these observations will be of the highest importance in developing meteorology and in extending our knowledge of terrestrial magnetism." This recommendation caused the convening of the International Polar Conference at Hamburg, October 1, 1879. Doctor Neumayer was president, and eleven nations pledged their support. The schedule of optional and obligatory observations was submitted and approved.

As enumerated, fifteen stations were occupied, while thirty-four permanent observatories adopted the schedule. This raised the number of coöperating stations to forty-nine, a most notable instance of international scientific action.

The Austrian-Hungarian expedition to Jan Mayen, at the expense of Count Wilczek, was commanded by Lieutenant Emil von Wohlgemuth. The *Pola*, after several attempts, made harbor at Mary Muss Bay, where the station was established July, 1882. Besides making the complete sets of observations until August 4, 1883, the observers charted and explored the island (Wohlgemuth: "Osterreichische Polarstation Jan Mayen." 3 vols. Wien).

Denmark, through Professor A. F. W. Paulsen, occupied Godthaab, Greenland, from August 1, 1882, to August 31, 1883. Special observations were made in atmospheric electricity, temperatures of rocks and earth, and the parallax of auroras was measured (Paulsen: "Expedition Danoise, Godthaab." 2 vols. Copenhagen).

The Danish steamer *Dijmphna*, commanded by Lieutenant A. P. Hovgaard, was beset in Kara Sea, 71° N., 64° E., where he supplemented the obligatory observations by others on the chlorides and salts of the sea. She escaped through Waigat Strait September, 1883.

Finland maintained a station at Sodankyla, 67° 24' N., 27° E., from August 29, 1882, to September 1, 1883. Special observations were made of the aurora, and in connection therewith an auroral station was established at Kautokeino, under S. Tromholt (Lemstrom and Biese: "Expedition Polaire Finlandaise." 3 vols. Helsingfors).

France decided on an antarctic station, near Cape Horn. Lieutenant Courcelle-Seneuil located at Orange Bay, 55° 31' S., 70° 21' W., and occupied it from September 6, 1882, to September 3, 1883. Besides the obligatory work, there were brought back seventy cases of specimens, — anthropological, botanical, ethnographic, geological and zoölogical. These collections have been classified, studied and discussed in a manner most creditable to French scientists. The eight published volumes, in typographical beauty, are unequaled by any other international polar works (Hyades, Lephay, Cannellier *et al.*: "Mission Scientific du Cap Horn." 8 vols. 1885–1891).

[211]

Germany established an arctic and an antarctic station, while the observatories at Breslau and Gottingen coöperated. The arctic station, under Doctor W. Giese, at Kingawa Fiord, 66° 36' N., 67° 19' W., was maintained from July, 1882, to August, 1883. By the aid of the Moravians, supplementary observations were made in Labrador by Doctor K. R. Koch. Giese and L. Ambronn also explored regions adjacent to the station. The antarctic station, on South Georgia, was occupied from September, 1882, to August, 1883. The expedition under Doctor K. Schrader was quartered at Royal Bay, where the surrounding conditions were unfavorable to extended survey of the island (Neumayer and Borgen: "Beobachtungs-Ergebnisse der Deutsche Stationenen." 2 vols. I, "Kingua Fjord"; II, "Sud-Giorgen." 1886).

Holland planned a station at Dicksonhavn, on the arctic coast of Asia, under Doctor M. Snellen. His steamer *Varna* was beset September, 1882, in Kara Sea, and was finally wrecked June 24, 1883. With commendable spirit Snellen continued observations until August 1, when the party by boat and sledge reached safely Novaya Zemlya, all in health (Snellen an Volck: "De Nederlandsche Pool-Expeditien." 1886).

The Norwegian station, at Bossekop, 69° 56' N., 23° E., was maintained under A. S. Steen from June, 1882, to August, 1883 (Steen: "Der Norwegischen Polarstation Bossekop in Alten." 1888).

Under the auspices of the Imperial Russian Geographical Society, a station under Lieutenant Jurgens was established in the Lena delta. Located on Sagaztyr Island 73° 23' N., 124° E, it was occupied from August, 1882, to July, 1883. Jurgen mapped the delta (Lenz and Eigner: "Beobachtungen der Russischen Polarstation an der Lenamunding." 2 vols. 1886–1895).

The other Russian station was located at Little Karmakul Bay, Novaya Zemlya, and occupied from August, 1882, to August, 1883. Commanded by Lieutenant C. Andrejeff, besides its observations, the personnel crossing the island made botanical and zoölogical studies (Andrejeff and Lenz: "Beobachtungen der Russischen Polarstation auf Nowaja Semla." 2 vols. 1886–1891).

Unfavorable navigation prevented Sweden from locating its station at the northernmost cape of Spitsbergen. Doctor Ekholm therefore established it at Cape Thorsden, Ice Fiord, 78° 28' N., 16° E., and made observations from August, 1882, to August, 1883 (Ekholm *et al.*: "Observations par l'Expedition Suedoise, Cap Thorsden." 2 vols. 1885–1894. See also Solander: "Observations du Magnetisme a Upsula." 1893).

The United States occupied two stations. That under Lieutenant P. H. Ray was located at Point Barrow, where obligatory observations were made from September, 1881, to August, 1883. Aid was extended to the crew of a wrecked whaler,

North Star; ethnographic studies made of the Eskimos; collections were made of the fauna and flora, while Ray in his personal explorations discovered Meade River and the Meade Mountain range (Ray: "Report of Expedition to Point Barrow." 1885; also Murdoch: "Ethnological Results of the Point Barrow Expedition", in 9th annual Report Bureau of Ethnology. 1892).

The American expeditions were first in the field through the indefatigable exertions of Captain H. W. Howgate, U. S. Army, who sent forth the preliminary *Gulnare* expedition of 1880, which failed to reach Lady Franklin Bay.

The station nearest the Pole was that at Lady Franklin Bay, 81° 44′ N., 64° 45′ W., commanded by Lieutenant A. W. Greely, U. S. Army, where observations were made from August, 1881, to August, 1883. Besides the obligatory observations, studies were made of auroras, arctic ice, gravity, tides and other oceanic conditions. Collections were made relative to fauna, flora, geology and ethnography. Although the geographic discoveries were most important, not being strictly scientific they are described in Chapter VIII.

The results of the scientific studies of the Greely expedition have special importance owing to the very high latitude in which they were made. The systematic and continuous readings of the magnetic instruments enabled experts to accurately calculate the secular variation of the magnetic declination

RUSSIAN POST IN MATOCHKIN SHAR, NOVAYA ZEMLYA. RADIO STATION
BROADCASTING WEATHER REPORTS DAILY.

for the regions of Smith Sound, which were then erroneously charted. The meteorological data at the station, supplemented by field observations, made possible the determination of the climatic conditions of Grinnell Land, where a fertile region lies between two ice-capped highlands. The tidal records at Lady Franklin Bay, together with those made on the shores of the ice-covered sea, have enabled scientists not only to determine the cotidal lines of the Arctic Ocean, but also to make the remarkable discovery that the diurnal inequality of the tidal wave conforms at Lady Franklin Bay to the sidereal day. The tidal observations also indicated that Greenland ended near 84° north; and further, that the Arctic Ocean is a deep sea, — with a narrow continental shelf, — a view corroborated by sea soundings off the west coast of Hazen Land. The pendulum swings, the most northerly ever made, are classed by authority as "far the best that have ever been made within the Arctic Circle (and the) determination of gravity (therefrom) has been singularly successful."

The annual visiting ship promised for the years 1882 and 1883 did not arrive, and Greely faced the abandonment of the station. There arose the alternative — to remain a third year with the necessity of living on the game of the country, or retreat by boats. To ensure the safety of the scientific work, all observations were reduced for instrumental errors, means calculated, and records

[215]

made in duplicate; thus one set, in waterproof case, would be carried in each boat. Similar protection and distribution of the standard instruments was arranged.

The point to be reached was Cape Sabine, about two hundred miles in a straight course, but double the distance by the coast which must be skirted in the floe-covered sea. It was a longer boat journey than had ever been made through arctic ice. This, too, through straits where the *Polaris* had been lost in its southward voyage, and where the stout sealer, *Proteus*, had been crushed three weeks earlier. Experts had declared such a journey impossible. In February, before the sun returned, stores of food and fuel were laid down as far south as the sledge party could safely travel.

The bay ice broke August 9, 1883, and the journey immediately began. The voyage was made under most adverse conditions: the straits were jammed with ice, severe gales recurred, high spring tides were running, so that the heavy floes were kept in violent motion against the precipitous, rocky shores. Yet in sixteen days Cape Hawks was reached after a journey of some four hundred miles; Sabine was in sight, distant only some twenty miles, and they hoped to reach it in a day.

But that very day winter temperatures set in, the open ice pack solidified and the boats were beset beyond escape. Later the party sought to reach land by sledge, — Greenland or Sabine,

[216]

as the floes moved to and fro. Adverse weather in the shape of snow-filled blizzards, with high winds, caused such violent movements of the floes that it required nineteen days of sledging to reach land, only thirteen miles distant when they started. However, on September 29, after having made in fifty days a journey exceeding five hundred miles in distance, the party landed near Cape Sabine. Every man was in health, the records and instruments were in perfect condition.

In a cache was a record signed by Lieutenant E. A. Garlington, informing Greely that the relief ship, *Proteus*, had sunk in the ice north of the Cape on July 23, 1883. The expected depôt had not been landed, and there were available only trifling stores, which Garlington had been unable to carry away in his retreating boats.

His record said in part: "Boat at Isabella (there was none), U. S. S. *Yantic* on her way to Littleton Island, with orders not to enter the ice. I will endeavor to communicate with these vessels at once. Everything in the power of man will be done to rescue the (Greely's) brave men."

It transpired that there was no boat at Isabella, that Garlington's order to replace damaged caches was disobeyed; that he had no knowledge of the safety of the cache at Littleton Island; that he took every pound of food he could carry, though advised that Greely was provisioned only to August, 1883; that when he reached the *Yantic* safely he did not even ask Wilde (the naval commander) to go north and lay down food for Greely, otherwise doomed to starvation. As for Commander Wilde, U. S. Navy, he sailed south, stating that he had no fear but Greely could care for his party.

In mid-October the party established Camp Clay, on Bedford Pym Island, erecting a hut of rocks, canvas, boat and snow slabs. Land game was sought, and seal holes watched to supplement the food (enough for only forty days) which was needed for two hundred fifty days before aid came. Efforts to cross Smith Sound failed, and no game was found, save occasionally. However, exploration discovered Rice Strait, Pym Island, and a new land (Schley) which succeeding explorers quietly renamed. The party was in rags and fuel was wanting—conditions which imposed hardships during the one hundred forty-five days without the sun, and two hundred forty continuous days on which the temperature remained below freezing. When food failed, existence was eked out by seal thongs, plants, saxifrage flowers, seaweed, sand fleas and lichens. Courage and solidarity were maintained, until June 22, 1884, when the navy squadron ships *Thetis* and *Bear*, under Captain W. S. Schley and Commander W. H. Emory, rescued the eight living men. To commemorate this service, Donald MacMillan erected on Pym Island, a tablet thus inscribed: "To the memory of the dead, who, under Lieutenant A. W. Greely, here gave their lives to ensure the final and complete success of the First Scientific Coöperation of the United States with other Nations, 1881–1884. Erected by the National Geographic Society, 1925 " (Greely : " Proceedings of United States Expedition to Lady Franklin Bay." 2 vols. 1888 ; and Greely : "Three Years of Arctic Service." 1885).

CHAPTER XXI

THE ANTARCTIC REGIONS IN GENERAL

UNTIL the end of the nineteenth century there had not been sufficient exploration of the area within the antarctic circle to justify extended consideration of the subject as a whole, although isolated efforts and results were of importance. The reasons for this seeming neglect of the south-polar regions are not difficult of justification.

The lands within the arctic circle are not alone contiguous to powerful and enterprising nations, but they are also so favored by climate and soil as to present suitable conditions for animal and plant life. Indeed Arctic America, Asia and Europe have large habitable districts where human activities now present life environments not always harsh and forbidding, but in places attractive and productive. In addition the northern seas, filled with abundant life, furnish subsistence and wealth to thousands of daring men who annually seek their accessible waters.

At the other pole of the world we find the antarctic region to be a veritable land of desolation, — forbidding, uninhabitable and in places inaccessible. Its northern confines and surroundings are largely oceanic, where freezing temperatures, violent snow blizzards and other winter conditions are not unusual in midsummer. While in high latitudes around the South Pole there are extended land areas, doubtless forming a continent, yet these are sterile regions, overlain by ice coverings of vast extent and enormous thickness.

It is doubtful if one per cent. of Antarctic lands is ever ice-free, so that ordinary forms of land life are entirely wanting. There are no human communities south of Cape Horn, more than two thousand miles from the Pole, though the Argentine Government maintains a weather outpost at Scotia Bay, South Georgia, whose force is changed annually. Within the circle, animal life and vegetable life on land are practically absent, save a few low forms of hardy lichens and mosses. No plant life there gladdens the eye, except two species on Graham Land; even the hum of insects is unheard, as the terrestrial fauna consists of wingless species. Curiously enough, sea life is more abundant than in other oceans, the higher forms being whales, seals and wonderful birds, — skuas, penguins and petrels. Owing to distance, dangers and expense, these were comparatively undisturbed until the inventions and enterprise of the twentieth century made their pursuit and capture a remunerative industry.

The geographic evolution of the south-polar world has passed through three distinct phases:

first, imaginative and exaggerated presentations; second, casual examination and neglect; and lastly accidental rediscovery, followed by carefully planned explorations and thorough scientific research.

One of the results of Magellan's voyage of 1520 was the reconstruction of world maps in general, and of antarctic maps in particular, to conform with the widely increased geographic knowledge of the earth. Fact and fancy then played not unequal parts in many geographical works, a practice not unknown in the twentieth century. Among other presentations, by inference and extension, at the end of the mediaeval age are those of Ortelius, who in his "Typus orbis terrarum", 1570, first charted the mythical Magellanic continent under the inscription *Terra australis non dum cognita*. This supposititious southern land was represented as covering the entire area from the forty-fifth parallel to the Pole. In the region of Magellan Strait, Tierra del Fuego was considered part of an unexplored continent, which, near the Javan archipelago, was extended as far northward as latitude 15° S.

Sir Francis Drake, rounding Cape Horn in 1577, not only proved Tierra del Fuego to be a separate archipelago, but also made it for two centuries "the uttermost part of the land towards the South Pole." Wytfliet in 1598 says of these regions: "The *Australias Terra*, the most southern of all lands, begins at one or two degrees from the equator, and is ascertained by some to be of so great an extent that if it were thoroughly explored it would be regarded as a fifth part of the world."

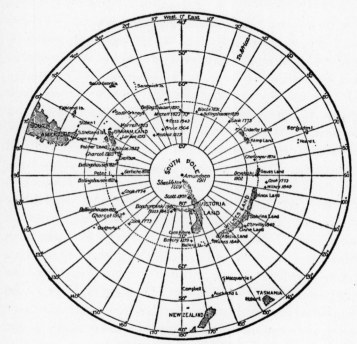

ANTARCTIC REGIONS

Even Tasman's discovery of Tasmania in 1642 only pushed the land southward without destroying faith in its existence, and Kerguelen-Trémarec in 1772 considered Kerguelen Island in 49° N., 70° E., as part of the mythical continent.

[223]

The geographic importance of the problem was set forth in the stirring dedication of "Dalrymple's Travels", 1770: "To the man who, emulous of Magalhaens and the heroes of former times (undeterred by difficulties and unseduced by pleasure), shall persist through every obstacle, and, not by chance but by virtue and good conduct, succeed in establishing an intercourse with a southern continent."

To the great navigator James Cook was entrusted the solution of the Magellanic continent, and he prosecuted the search with the skill and assiduity that marked all his voyages, with the *Adventure* (Captain Furneaux) and *Resolute*. Sailing from Cape of Good Hope November 22, 1772, Cook sought in vain the reported land of Bouvet in 54° 15' S., 6° 11' E., which is really in 54° 26' S., 3° 24' E. Turning southeast, Cook was the first to cross the antarctic circle, attaining 67° 15' S., 38° E., whence, forced back by an impenetrable ice pack, he returned to New Zealand without discovering land in his voyage of 177 days and 11,000 miles. It is improbable that he saw the ice barrier, but his experience with tabular bergs, sixty feet high and two miles in circumference, disclosed the fearful and hitherto unsuspected magnitude of antarctic ice.

In November, 1773, Cook renewed from New Zealand his southern explorations with a single ship, the *Adventure*. He crossed the antarctic

circle December 20 in 147° W., but was obliged
to recross it in 142° 54′ W., from 67° 31′ S. Following a zigzag course, he again passed it January
26, 1774, and attained 71° 10′ S., 106° 54′ W.
The conditions which necessitated his return were
of special interest. South of him was a compact
ice field, ranging east and west, from which rose
in various places mountains of ice, to a height far
beyond any hitherto seen. In January, 1775, he
discovered the Sandwich group, of which Thule
Island, 59° 14′ S., 27° 45′ W., was then the most
southerly known land. It is interesting to note
that his antarctic latitude practically coincides
with his arctic northing of 71° 08′ N., a record
of the nearest approach to the two poles.

Cook's antarctic achievements would be viewed
as remarkable in the twentieth century of steam,
and they excite the greatest admiration of all
navigators, as they were made under sail. He
circumnavigated the Southern Ocean, surpassed
by six hundred miles the highest latitude of his
predecessors, crossed the antarctic circle at four
widely separated points, demonstrated south of
the 56th parallel (previously the most southerly
region known) the nonexistence of land to the
very borders of the circle, and disclosed the existence of a great ocean, wherein were ice conditions
on a scale of magnificence and importance hitherto
unsuspected. He said: "We saw ice-mountains,
whose lofty summits were lost in the clouds. I

was now fully satisfied that there was no Southern Continent."

Cook was in a measure justified in his opinion that he had put "an end to the search for a southern continent, which had engrossed the attention of the maritime nations for two centuries." In fact, he had merely postponed further search for half a century, and was destined to be surpassed in general antarctic explorations by his immediate successor, a distinguished Russian seaman.

Bellingshausen, sailing in 1819 with Lazareff in the *Vostok* and *Mirny*, far surpassed Cook in extent of work, although not equaling his latitude by seventeen miles. Bellingshausen not only circumnavigated the globe to the south of the 60th parallel, but also traversed seventy degrees of longitude within the circle, which he entered at six widely separated points. His positions were: 2° 15′ E., 69° 21′ S.; 18° E., 69° 06′ S.; 41° E., 66° 53′ S.; 162° W., 67° 30′ S.; 120° W., 67° 50′ S.; 92° 10′ W., 69° 53′ S.

His intrepidity and perseverance, under adverse conditions of ice and weather, resulted in important contributions to the world's knowledge of southern seas, and restricted materially the possible limits of continental land. He had, however, the honor of first discovering land within the antarctic circle, — Peter I Land in 90° W., and Alexander I Land in 73° W.

Further discoveries will be considered in later chapters on the separate quadrants.

THE CONTINENT OF ANTARCTICA

Among the distinguished scientists who have attempted, on relatively scanty data, to theoretically outline geographically the extended land areas of the antarctic regions, Sir John Murray, of the *Challenger* expedition, was the most advanced and definite. Basing his theory on a study of sediments from the southern seas, he outlined a southern continent, which he christened Antarctica. Although some scientists believe that the continent is divided into two great ice-capped lands, most attentive and authoritative students accept Murray's conclusion.

Extended explorations by Bruce, Charcot, Davis, Drygalski, Gerlache, Mawson, Nordenskiold, Scott, Shackleton and others have contributed such wealth of data as makes it possible to give a general outline of the continent of Antarctica. It is in several respects the most remarkable of the continents, in its towering mass, its geological history, its unique isolation, its climatic conditions, its physical features and its scantiness of life forms.

Its area is estimated at 5,122,000 square miles. Its average elevation is nearly six thousand feet, double that of any other continent. The south-polar plateau approaches eleven thousand feet above the sea, and its great mountain ranges rise

[227]

to heights ranging from eleven thousand to fifteen thousand feet. Its continental coast lines are approximately fourteen thousand miles in length, of which only five thousand have been visited and barely three thousand five hundred even casually surveyed (David: "Antarctica." *Geographical Journal*, June, 1914).

Remarkable as are the ice caps of Greenland and Northeast Land, they sink into insignificance compared with that of Antarctica. This polar ice sheet enshrouds the continent — entirely it may be said since scarcely one per cent. is ice-free — scattered nunitaks (bare peaks projecting), and portions of the loftiest mountains. The ice is amazing, not alone in its extent but in its thickness, which has been estimated to be from two thousand to five thousand feet. Nor has nature been content to conceal the land only, for the ice sheet covers in unbroken form thousands of square miles of the Southern Ocean, — a process that it has required many hundred years to accomplish, and which in completed form makes it for hundreds of miles impossible to determine where the land ends and the sea begins.

Of these false coasts or barriers, two require notice. East of Victoria Land, Ross Barrier is formed by ice streams from Beardmore and other glaciers. It has a sea front of four hundred miles, with cliffs rising from twenty to one hundred and fifty feet. From the apex of the barrier to the sea is nearly four hundred miles; the march seaward is so slow that it has been calculated it takes one thousand two hundred years for the ice to move from the Beardmore glacier to the sea. In its maximum stage the barrier extended some two hundred miles farther into the ocean, and had an elevation eight hundred feet above the present surface.

Nearly as remarkable is the barrier discovered by Mawson (Mawson: "The Home of the Blizzard." 1915), where the inland ice, known as the Watson Glacier, or the Shackleton Ice Shelf, extends outward one hundred twenty miles in unbroken form over the sea.

Geology tells us that Antarctica has not always been ice-clad, without vegetation and perhaps life. There are vast deposits of coal, extending one thousand four hundred miles from the ranges on Victoria Land to the sandstone nunivak of King George Land. Shackleton found fossil wood and rootlets, and Scott brought back fossil leaves. Priestly found large pieces of wood, apparently coniferous. David questions: "Could this coal-flora have flourished, even under warmer conditions, with the Beardmore glacier area situated in its present relation to the South Pole, so that the flora would have been in darkness for five months of the year? If not, has the Pole shifted? This is a problem for the botanists and geophysicists" (Taylor: "Geology of East Ant-

arctica." *Geographical Journal*, October, 1914).
In marvelous contrast are the many volcanos,
some yet active.

Altogether, Antarctica presents physical problems which the acutest minds of the twentieth
century will have difficulty in solving.

CHAPTER XXII

THE AFRICAN (ENDERBY) QUADRANT
(*From Greenwich to 90° East*)

THE most convenient topical method of treating antarctic explorations in detail is by quadrants. These quadrants by American designation are geographical, but the English have given them personal names, those of British explorers. The African or Enderby Quadrant covers longitudes from Greenwich to 90° E.; the Australian or Victoria Quadrant from 90° E., to 180° E.; the American or Weddell Quadrant from Greenwich to 90° W.; the Pacific or Ross Quadrant from 90° W. to 180° W.

Explorations in the African Quadrant were probably due to the dictum of Charles de Brosses, who predicted that "the most celebrated of modern sovereigns will be he who gives his name to the Southern World." France in 1772 sent Lozier-Bouvet, who passed through 50 degrees of longitude south of the 50th parallel. He found no continent, but discovered Bouvet Island, 54° 26' S., 3° 24' E. The same year Marion-Dufresne discovered the Marion and Crozet islands, and Kerguelen-Trémarec discovered Kerguelen Island, 49° 40' S., 69° 30' E.

As shown in Chapter XXI, Cook reached in 1772, 67° 15' S., 38° E. Bellingshausen, February 6, 1820, reached 69° 06' S., 16° E.; he measured an iceberg between 375 and 408 feet high.

Most notable explorations were those of John Biscoe, who crossed the antarctic circle in 1° E., and on January 28, 1831, reached 69° S., 10° 43' E. Skirting the ice pack six weeks, Biscoe, on February 28, "clearly distinguished land (Enderby) of considerable extent . . . being the black tops of mountains showing through the snow . . . a great distance (thirty miles) off, completely beset with close field ice and icebergs." Naming it Cape Ann, he located it in 66° 25' S., 49° 18' E. Striving against difficulties, he neared the land again on March 16 and saw a high mountain near Cape Ann. He sailed his small brig, *Tula*, nearly 90 degrees of longitude south of the 60th parallel. (*See* also the American Quadrant.) R. H. Mill recites the discovery, in 1833, of Kemp Land, 66° S., 58° to 60° E., by a British sealer of that name. The voyage for magnetic surveys by Moore, in 1844, reached 67° 50' S., 39° 41' E., but made no discoveries. Moore, however, on March 7, 1844, believed that he saw land, a high ridge, in 64° S., about 49° E.

The demands of science caused the *Challenger* expedition for biological and physical explorations of the deep sea. Under George S. Nares the *Challenger*, first of steamships to cross the circle,

reached on February 16, 1874, 66° 40′ S., 78° 22′ E.
Though the *Challenger* barely entered the circle,
her researches contributed in an unparalleled
degree to a knowledge of the south-polar regions.
Murray (Murray: "Results of the Challenger
Expedition") records ninety species of animals
unknown in tropical seas, which are common to
the northern and southern oceans. Murray and
Buchan demonstrated that high barometric pressures cover Antarctica. Marine fauna was
dredged with a wealth unequaled in other waters.
Glaciated rock fragments told the story of the
foundations of antarctic lands, since they are not
found in islands.

The German scientific deep-sea expedition of
1898, in the *Valdavia*, commanded by Krech, did
valuable work, through Chun and Schott. It
located Bouvet Island, not seen for seventy-five
years. At their farthest, 64° 15′ S., 54° 20′ E.,
within 102 miles of Enderby Land, the sea was
2,540 fathoms deep. They made the maximum
sounding in south polar waters, 3,134 fathoms.
There were seen together 180 bergs, one 10 miles
long, another 190 feet high. Their dredging
showed continental rocks, granites, schist and red
sandstone (Chun: "Aus den Tiefen des Welt-
meeres." 1900).

The German scientific expedition of 1901, in
the *Gauss*, under Drygalski, disclosed the nonexistence of Termination Land in its assigned

[233]

position. On February 22, 1902, after the ocean rapidly shallowed from 3,300 to 250 fathoms, Drygalski saw an entirely ice-clad land, with a high vertical ice-cliff sea front. Attempting to trace the coast westward, the *Gauss* was beset for a year. In five months' sledging they carefully explored Gauss-berg, forty-six miles distant, and Kaiser Wilhelm II Land, which was of considerable size and entirely ice-clad. It extended from 87° E. to 94° E., joining, as is now known, Queen Mary Land of Mawson. Soundings resulted in "the demonstration of a trough over 4,500 metres deep, running between the Crozet Islands and Kerguelen, and connecting the abysses of the Indian Ocean with a deep ravine on the outer edge of the Austral sea" (Drygalski: "Zum Kontinent des eisigen Sudens." 1904).

The authenticity of Benjamin Morrell's "Four Voyages", 1832, has been seriously questioned. Doubtless the longitudes were often inaccurate. He reported no land, did not surpass his predecessors in latitude, and makes no claims. Possibly he may have been west of Enderby Land, near points reached by Biscoe and Moore.

CHAPTER XXIII

THE AUSTRALIAN (VICTORIA) QUADRANT

(*From 90° East to 180° East*)

ALTHOUGH neither of the great south-polar circumnavigators, Cook and Bellingshausen, entered the antarctic circle in this quadrant, yet it was destined to be the theater of the most active and successful efforts to increase the knowledge of Antarctica.

First to enter these unknown waters was an English sealer, John Balleny, in the *Eliza*, with Freeman in the *Sabrina*. Balleny crossed the circle in 172° E., 69° S., 220 miles beyond Bellingshausen's latitude on this meridian.

On February 9, 1839, Balleny discovered five (Balleny) islands, in 164° 29′ E., 66° 37′ S. He says: "Saw the appearance of land to the S. W.; at 8 P.M. got within 5 miles of it, when we saw another piece of land of great height, bearing w. by s. February 10. At 2 A.M. bore up for (the middle island) and got within half a mile, but found it completely icebound, with high perpendicular cliffs . . . . I make the high western points of the middle island, to be 66° 44′ S., 163° 11′ E. Feb. 11. Saw the land bearing about w.s.w., and of a tremendous height, at least 12,000 feet and covered with snow."

"Feb. 12. Went ashore at the only place likely to afford a landing. It proved only the drawback of the sea, leaving a beach of 3 or 4 feet at most. Freeman jumped out and got a few stones. But for the bare rocks where the icebergs had broken from we should have scarce have known it for land at first, but we plainly perceived smoke arising from the mountain tops. The cliffs are perpendicular, and what in all probability would have been valleys and beaches are occupied by solid blocks of ice." The voyage of Balleny outlined the route by which Ross attained his notable success.

France was next in this field, its expedition of 1837 being for discovery and research. The squadron of *Astrolabe* and *Zélée*, under Dumont D'Urville, sailed from Hobart Town on January 1, 1840, after research in the American quadrant. On January 20 (ship's date which should have been 21) D'Urville reports: "Before us rose the Land (Cape Découverte); one could distinguish its details. Its aspect was very uniform. Entirely covered with snow, it stretched from east to west and seemed to drop towards the sea by an easy incline. In the midst of its uniform grayish tint we could see no peak, no single black spot. On one of ten islets, near the mainland, no vegetation was found, although frequented by penguins. This region, Adélie Land, in 66° 30′ S., 138° 21′ E., trended from s.e. to n.w., and was skirted to 155° 30' E. Its sea face consisted of high vertical ice-cliffs, while the interior was ice-covered, rounded and without any marked peak."

Following a violent gale, the squadron reached to the westward, on January 30, Côte Clarie, in 131° E., 64° 30' S. D'Urville reported: "We saw a cliff with a uniform height of 100 to 150 feet. Spent all day sailing 20 to 25 leagues along this ice-bound coast, without seeing any peak rising above the snow plains. (The land) was perfectly vertical at the edge (of the sea) and horizontal at the top, not the smallest irregularity, not the slightest eminence. In vain we scanned carefully all the contours, trying to discover some rock or sign of land."

The United States pursued its antarctic work contemporaneously with France. Under an Act of Congress Charles Wilkes commanded a squadron that sailed for general maritime exploration, whose work in the western hemisphere is recited under appropriate quadrants.

In operating from Australia, Wilkes had four wretchedly outfitted and entirely unsuitable vessels for such work, — the *Vincennes*, 780 tons; *Peacock*, 650 tons; *Porpoise*, 230 tons; and *Flying Fish*, 96 tons. On January 13, 1840, Ringgold, *Vincennes*, thought that land was visible from 65° 08' S., 163° E., — to date neither disproved nor substantiated. January 16, the *Peacock* in 157° 46'

[237]

E., distinctly saw land "stretching to the s.w." Rudmose Brown charts it as "Cape Hudson"; if seen it must have been an outer cape of either King George V Land of Mawson, or of Oates Land.

The discovery on January 19 was the most important and is unquestioned, being verified by D'Urville and Mawson. Wilkes, on the *Vincennes*, reports that between 8 and 9 A.M., from 154° 30′ E., 66° 20′ S., "Land was now certainly visible from the *Vincennes*, both to the s.s.e. and s.w., in the former direction most distinctly. Both appeared high. This part of Antarctica was thus discovered by Wilkes one day earlier than the discovery of D'Urville. Wilkes was fully justified in his action a few days later in saying: "I gave the land the name of the Antarctic Continent."

Wilkes continued his explorations despite the severity of the weather, and the unseaworthiness of the *Vincennes*, while his officers unavailingly urged his return. Between January 23 and February 14 he skirted the ice cliffs and pack along the coast of Antarctica about 150° E. to 97° E., 64° S. Excerpts indicate the results: "Reached the solid barrier. An indentation of 25 miles width we explored to the depth of about 15 miles. . . . Reached the ice-barrier and hove to. . . . Approached within half a mile of dark volcanic rocks, which appeared on both sides of us. . . . Beyond (the barrier, about 150 feet high) the outline of the high land could be well dis-

The Great Antarctic Ice Barrier in 1841, Varying from 160 to 250 Feet above the Sea. Discovered by Sir James C. Ross.

tinguished. . . . (Land about 20) miles distant, a lofty mountain range covered with snow. By measurement the coast of the Antarctic Continent, then in sight, 75 miles, entirely covered with snow. . . . Land about 8 miles distant was seen."

Ross, his successor, criticized Wilkes bitterly and omitted his discoveries from the south-polar chart. Ross expressly asserts the certain accuracy of his own discoveries "where no part has been laid down upon mere appearances." It is the irony of fate that his countryman Scott should not only have proven the nonexistence of the Parry Mountains of Ross, but also that his assumed discovery of three new islands should really be simply a single island whose three peaks had been previously discovered and charted by another countryman, Balleny. One understands the bitter feelings of Ross when a competitor had discovered a new continent, but his criticisms are a blemish on his otherwise high reputation. Unfortunately Wilkes also had his faults, and doubtless some of his longitudes and charted regions were somewhat erroneous. Rudmose Brown, a recognized geographical expert of the highest standing (Rudmose Brown: "The Polar Regions." 1927), in view of the explorations of Drygalsi and Davis, charts the continent of Antarctica along the antarctic circle westward from Wilkes in 145° E., to 100° E., and gives his name to part of the coast.

The most extended discoveries made in this

quadrant were those of James C. Ross who, commanding the *Erebus* and *Terror*, and profiting by Balleny's discoveries, crossed the antarctic circle on January 1, 1841, in about 174° E.

Entering what is now known as Ross Sea, he discovered Victoria Land, and sailed southward along its ice-encumbered western coast to Mt. Erebus, 77° 40' S., an active volcano. From it Ross in one instance saw "flame and smoke being projected to a great height." Erebus was thought to be on the mainland; in reality it is on Ross Island. Of the interior Ross reported: "We could not see anything except the summit of a lofty range of mountains (named by him Parry Mountains) extending southward as far as the seventy-ninth degree of latitude." Scott proved that this must have been a mirage, as such mountains are nonexistent. Victoria Land is, however, a glacier-clad country, bordered by a moving ice belt then impassible. Ross landed on Franklin and Possession islands: finding no vegetation, he wrongly concluded there was none in the antarctic regions. By magnetic observations Ross placed the south magnetic pole about five hundred miles to the southwest; as a matter of fact it lies to the eastward. Its location was determined by David, of the Shackleton expedition (1908–1909), to be in 72° 25' S., 155° 16' E.

Progress beyond Mt. Erebus being impossible, Ross turned to the east, and discovered an immense glacial stream flowing into the sea, which he appropriately named the (Ross) Barrier. The sea face of the barrier was composed of vertical ice cliffs as high as 250 feet, though in a great indentation where the ships entered, in 187° E., it was only 160 feet high.

Ross skirted the barrier, attained 78° 04' S., and on February 5 reached 167° W. On his homeward voyage he claimed to have discovered three new islands, — Russell Peak, Smyth and Francis. It was found by Scott that what Ross saw were three peaks of one of the islands discovered by Balleny (Ross: "Voyage in the Southern and Antarctic Regions." 2 vols. 1847).

James C. Ross contributed to the glory of his country, and gained fame by his scientific and geographic researches in both the arctic and antarctic researches, in this and other quadrants. His errors of observation and conclusion are such as have marked the careers of other great explorers, and are not to be seriously criticized.

The next ship to enter Ross Sea was the whaler *Antarctic*, Captain Kristensen, which reached Coulman Island, 74° S., on January 22, 1895. Its primary importance was the discovery of lichens on Possession Island and at Cape Adare. This controverted the opinion of Ross and confirmed that of Palmer as to the existence of vegetation on antarctic lands.

The first wintering on Antarctica was that of

Borchgrevinck, with a party of ten, at Cape Adare 1899–1900. Land explorations were largely failures, but regular and valuable work was done in magnetism, meteorology, and allied sciences. Jensen, who had taken Borchgrevinck south in the *Southern Cross*, returned in 1900, when the east coast of Victoria Land was definitely charted, Wood Bay increased in area, and reindeer moss found on Franklin Island and at Mt. Melbourne, Victoria Land. It was discovered that Ross Barrier had receded about thirty miles since 1841. The *Southern Cross* was thus able to reach 78° 21′ S., and mooring at a low place in the sea face of the barrier, Borchgrevinck and Colbeck were enabled to journey south on the glacier to 78° 50′ S.

THE CONQUEST OF THE SOUTH POLE

With the opening of the twentieth century there began in this quadrant a series of remarkable expeditions which ended in the attainment of the South Pole. First, in 1901, came the British expedition of R. F. Scott in the *Discovery*, with a force of experts, among whom were Shackleton, Armitage, Wilson and others. From winter quarters at McMurdo Bay, 77° 49′ S., 166° E., extensive explorations were made. In entering McMurdo Strait, Scott sailed over the position assigned by Ross to the Parry Mountains. He steamed along the Ross Barrier to the eastward, passing the farthest point of Ross and Borchgrevinck, and discovered a new land, named King Edward VII. Situated between 152° and 157° W., trending to the northeast, only a few projecting peaks appeared above its rounded snow-covered surface. Soundings along the barrier disclosed depths of three hundred fathoms, but they gradually shoaled to seventy fathoms in the extreme east. Turned back by heavy ice, the party made a landing at a low point in 164° W., from which Armitage made a short sledge journey to 78° 50′ S., where he made a balloon ascension. From this position nothing was visible to the south except an unbroken expanse of undulating glacier ice streams. It appeared that between Edward and Victoria lands there was an offshoot of the continental ice cap more than two hundred miles wide.

In his main explorations southward towards the Pole, Scott followed the ice stream to the east of Victoria Land, a flat surface marked by undulations and a few crevasses but favorable to travel. In fifty-nine days he made three hundred eighty miles, his farthest point, reached December 30, 1902, being 82° 17′ S. The safety of the party was endangered on its return trip by scurvy which attacked Shackleton.

Meanwhile Armitage and Skelton, sledging to Victoria Land, reached a point 130 miles inland, where the elevation was nine thousand feet. Scott later made a sledge journey to investigate Victoria Land, when in an outward journey of three hundred miles he reached 77° 39′ S., 146° 33′ E. He found an unbroken expanse of inland ice of almost unvarying levelness. The upper winds are generally westerly; the annual snowfall about five inches; the terrestrial fauna and flora are of low order and extremely scanty. Scott considered it "probable that the coast (of Victoria Land) runs more or less in a straight line from Cape North to Adélie Land" (Scott: "Voyage of the *Discovery*." 2 vols. 1905).

Shackleton in 1908 renewed the south-polar quest from a base at Cape Royds, Ross Island. His march was over the Ross Barrier, well out from Victoria Land. With Armitage, Marshall and Wild, Shackleton started October 28, each man leading a pony. It developed that the barrier was largely crevassed, which nearly caused the death of one man. New land, ice-clad mountains, greeted the explorers on November 22, but its unfavorable trend obliged them to quit the barrier in order to travel south.

Fortunately a gap afforded a nearly direct route to the Pole. It was a rough, steep glacier, honeycombed with dangerous ice chasms, so difficult that it necessitated double journeys. On December 7 their last pony plunged into a crevasse hundreds of feet deep, and its leader, Wild, only escaped through the breaking of a swingtree.

On December 8 they reached a great plateau, of an elevation of seven thousand four hundred feet, surrounded by sandstone cliffs with strata of coal. On Christmas Day they were in 85° 51' S., with an antarctic summer temperature of 48 degrees below freezing, at an elevation of nine thousand five hundred feet. Marching upgrade they camped January 6, 1909, at an elevation of ten thousand five hundred feet, in 88° 07' S., with a prospect of reaching the Pole. But a violent blizzard forced them to remain in their bags sixty hours, when they nearly perished of cold in a temperature of 70 degrees below freezing. When the gale broke, their food permitted only a short march which brought them within ninety-seven miles of the Pole, on January 9, in 88° 23' S., 163° E.

Of the environment Shackleton says: "Before us stretched the same white plain. Our glasses showed no signs of land, and we could safely assume that the South Pole was situated on this immense plateau, between 10,000 and 11,000 feet above the sea."

This route to the Pole, long considered to be entirely English, was next traversed by Amundsen. He established his base at Whale Bay, and camped on Ross Barrier in 164° W., 78° 48' S. With his dog teams he laid out advance depôts to 80° S. He made his final start on October 8, 1911, with five men, fifty-two dogs and four sledges and food for four months. The highest ice was 10,750 feet, in 87° 40' N., whence it descended slightly to the

South Pole, which was reached December 14, 1911. Three days were passed making observations, not only at the Pole but within a radius of ten miles. His tent was left, with a record of his observations and a Norwegian flag.

The British expedition under R. F. Scott, in the *Terra Nova*, established his winter quarters at McMurdo Sound in 1910, and laid out his depôts and made his south-polar march with ponies. His route was longer than that of his competitor, being 1,842 miles, the longest sledge journey ever made. He reached the Pole on January 18, 1912. His return march was fatal. First Evans was fatally injured. Later, when within 155 miles of his ship, the party was struck by a blizzard which made travel impossible, and food failed. To save food for his comrades, Oates walked out in the storm and perished. Scott, Wilson and Bowers died of starvation and exhaustion ("Scott's Last Expedition." 2 vols. 1913).

Tenacity and courage are rarely wanting in explorers, associated often with high spiritual qualities. The history of polar exploration affords no more affecting and inspiring examples of these lofty characteristics than the self-sacrifice of Oates, and the acquiescence of Scott in his last lines, recorded by him with benumbed fingers.

The next explorer to navigate Ross Sea was the Japanese Shirase, who landed January 16, 1912, at Whale Bay, Ross Barrier. He ascended the

[246]

barrier and sledging to the southeast reached an elevation of one thousand eight hundred feet at 80° 05′ S., 156° 27′ W. (*Geographical Journal* 40 : 220). Shirase later in his ship followed the coast from Edward Land, whose area he somewhat extended, to Biscoe Bay.

In 1912 the coöperating expedition, which Shackleton sent to Ross Sea, to meet him when he crossed from Coats Land to McMurdo Sound (see Chapter XXV), under MacIntosh, reached Cape Evans in the *Aurora*. On May 6, 1915, a violent gale tore the ship from her moorings, leaving ten men on Ross Island. The *Aurora* was beset and drifted helplessly for a year before she could escape from the pack. Learning the situation on his escape from the shipwrecked *Endurance* in Weddell Sea, Shackleton proceeded to New Zealand and organized a relief expedition under John K. Davis, the skilled ice navigator. Proceeding to Cape Evans in the *Aurora*, Davis rescued the seven living men, one of the party having died of illness, and two others perished in a blizzard. During the drift of the *Aurora* to the northwest, between August 23 and October 4, 1915, new land was frequently seen, which was named Oates Land. It is situated between Cape North and King George Land, and evidently is a part of the continental coast.

The expedition in 1911–1914 of Mawson to Adélie Land distinguished itself by geographic and

scientific researches. Davis in the *Aurora* landed
Mawson and his eighteen comrades in January,
1912, in 67° S., about 142° E., at Commonwealth
Bay, where the home station was established on
that remarkable sea glacier, the Shackleton Ice
Shelf. Mawson sent Wild on the *Aurora*, with
eight men, to take station four hundred miles to
the east, near Gaussberg; the ship returned home
for the winter.

The field work of Mawson's party was extraordinary, involving two thousand four hundred
miles of sledging; the journeys on King George
Land extended from 142° E., to 150° E., and southward to the 72d parallel. Scientifically the most
important journey was that of Davis in locating
the south magnetic pole in 72° 25′ S., 155° 16′ E.
King George Land is a glacial-covered region,
undulating and crevasse-marked; in one crevasse
Ninis perished and Mawson barely escaped the
same fate.

On Queen Mary Land, Wild was equally ener-
getic, and in his sledge trips of eight hundred miles
he thoroughly explored that region. One of his
journeys extended eastward to 99° E., near Gauss-
berg, Wilhelm Land. The parties were relieved
by the *Aurora*, Mawson in 1913, and Wild in 1914
(Mawson: "The Home of the Blizzard." 2 vols.
1914).

Davis in his three voyages did remarkable work.
His numerous soundings, through 55 degrees of

longitude, added greatly to the hydrographical knowledge of the Southern Ocean. He also practically outlined the northern shores of Antarctica between longitudes 104° and 128° E. (Davis: "With *Aurora* in the Antarctic." 1919).

An extraordinary discovery was the Shackleton Ice Shelf, on which Mawson placed his station. It is a glacier projecting more than a hundred miles into the ocean, from about 64° 10' S., to 66° 15' S., and longitudinally, in irregular width, from 95° E. to 102° E.

Portions of the quadrant have changed from a field of exploration to one of commercial importance. Practical sovereignty of the region is now exercised by Great Britain, since the activity of Norwegian whalers has demonstrated the value of the material wealth of the antarctic seas.

By an Order-in-Council, dated July 30, 1923, Great Britain created the Ross Dependency. By this Order the coasts of Ross Sea, with the adjacent islands and territories, between 160° east longitude and 150° west longitude, and south of the 60th degree of latitude, were proclaimed a British Settlement, and placed under the jurisdiction of the Governor General of New Zealand. Within this territory are the coasts of Victoria Land, Edward Land and Ross Sea. With the Falkland Islands Dependency, this brings under British sovereignty nearly one third of all antarctic regions, territory covering 120 degrees of longitude.

Fishing and hunting are permitted in the Dependency under licenses granted by New Zealand. Whaling has proved quite profitable, the value of the annual catch being $1,000,000 or more. This exercise of British sovereignty has led to protest and complications. In 1927 certain whalers planned to fish in Ross Sea without obtaining a license. Thereupon New Zealand enacted a law fining any whaler fishing without a license, and confiscating the vessel.

Since 1925 Great Britain has been making a scientific survey of the antarctic seas with reference to the migration and breeding methods of the marine life. The intent is to establish in its Dependencies such regulations as will best conserve marine life, now in danger of extermination.

CHAPTER XXIV

THE PACIFIC (ROSS) QUADRANT
(*From 90° West to 180° West*)

THIS quadrant is the southerly extension of the vast Pacific Ocean, after which it is named. Its strictly oceanic character is indicated by the fact that south of the 50th parallel there are but two tiny islands north of the circle, — Dougherty on the 120th meridian, and Nimrod on the 160th. It thence follows that it is the least known, as one third of the circle is in regions never crossed. Indeed, between 90° W., and 150° W., the Antarctic Zone has been entered only by Cook, 1773 and 1774; Bellingshausen, 1821; Walker and Ringgold, 1840; Gerlache, 1899; and Charcot, 1909.

Cook's entrance in 147° W., 1773, was followed next year by his astonishing southing of 71° 10′ S., 106° 54′ W., without finding any indications of land.

Crossing thrice into the antarctic regions, Bellingshausen here made his highest latitude and also discovered the first land in the quadrant. He reached 67° S., 164° 34′ W., on December 24, 1820; 67° 30′ S., 120° W., on January 11, 1821; and his farthest south, 69° 53′ S., 92° 19′ W., on January 21. His discovery of the first antarctic island is thus given by Mill: "An island loftier than any berg had come in view. It lay in 69° S., 90° W., the most southerly land yet discovered, and when, on 22 January (1821) the ships came as near the land as the ice permitted, its length was found to be about nine miles, its breadth four miles, and its height was estimated at 4,000 feet. The island rose abruptly from the ice-covered sea and, except for the cliffs and higher slopes, was entirely swathed in snow."

Bellingshausen named it Peter I, and another island described in the American Quadrant, Alexander I Land.

The incursion of Walker was due to instructions from Wilkes to surpass Cook's farthest, then known as *Ne plus ultra*. Walker commanded the small tender, *Flying Fish*, ninety-six tons, in which he sailed through an open pack to 70° S., 105° W., where he was turned back by heavy ice fields. His companion Ringgold, in the *Porpoise*, only reached 68° S., 95° 44' W.

The second voyage of the great polar navigator, J. C. Ross, reached a latitude that was for years a southern record. In an antarctic cruise of two months he reached 70° 30' S., 173° 10' W., on February 8, 1842, and twenty days later attained 78° 10' S., 161° 27' W. Here he was confronted by towering ice cliffs more than a hundred feet high, in front of which the sea was two hundred thirty fathoms deep.

While the remarkable (Ross) Barrier discovered by him and the King Edward VII Land of Scott are situated in this quadrant, they are so closely and intimately connected with other voyages in the Australian Quadrant that they are therewith described.

For the visit of Gerlache to this quadrant, see the American Quadrant, in which his explorations were mainly prosecuted.

In his expedition of 1908 Charcot, from his winter quarters in the American Quadrant (*q.v.*), in an extraordinarily successful voyage westward, surveyed one hundred twenty miles of new land, and followed the edge of the southern ice fields to 124° W., the longest inroad for nearly a century.

CHAPTER XXV

THE AMERICAN (WEDDELL) QUADRANT

(*From Greenwich to 90° West*)

THE geographical evolution of this quadrant began through an accidental discovery by a British trading ship, and was carried on by American sealers, a body of adventurous seamen whose pursuits and inclinations have led them to unknown seas, and resulted in polar discoveries which would have crowned with honor professional explorers.

The advantages of the Pacific Ocean as a fishing ground appealed early to Americans, five whalers entering it in 1791. Worth, in the *Beaver*, the first arrival, was ordered out of Lima and forbidden the coast by the Spanish authorities. Some did their fishing in the stormy seas of Tierra del Fuego, establishing their base on the northwest island, Desolation; others frequented the Falklands. The later named group was visited for sealing in 1815, as American ships returned the following summer laden with sea-elephant oil. The first clearances for the South Sandwich Islands, noted by Starbuck, were in 1819, the *Equator* and *Balaena*, of New Bedford, probably the first whalers to visit these islands.

While there is little doubt that whalers or sealers in the early years of the nineteenth century attained high southern latitudes, data are wanting in this respect. This belief finds justification in the record by Balch of Eldred landing on Louis Philippe Land in 1875–1876, and of Lind in 1880 following Gerlache Strait along the west coast to 66° S.

The South Shetlands were discovered and visited by W. Smith in 1819. On November 21, 1821, a British sealer, George Powell, discovered the South Orkneys, which temporarily were charted under the name of their discoverer. In 1820 Bransfield sighted the peak named for him, the first glimpse of the continent of Antarctica. Palmer, an American sealer, saw the mountain peaks of Palmer, which the English call Graham Land, in 1821. In 1822 and again in 1825, Palmer fished in these waters, and was the first man to land on the continent ("Fanning's Voyages." 1834).

The intrepid Russian, Bellingshausen, after sailing 28 degrees of longitude south of the antarctic circle, ended his phenomenal voyage by entering these waters in 1921, when he discovered Alexander Island.

In 1823 an adventurous British sealer, James Weddell, with the *Jane* and *Beaufoy* crossed the circle. Favored by an open sea, he reached on February 20, 74° 15′ S., 4° 17′ W., exceeding

Cook's latitude by 214 miles (Weddell: "Voyage towards the South Pole"). An American, Morrell, the same year reached 70° 14′ S., in an uncertain longitude, which he places at 40° W. (Morrell: "Four Voyages"). Pendleton and Palmer, in 1830, unsuccessfully sought land southwest of Cape Horn, seen by whalers Macy and Gardiner.

The French expedition of 1838, under D'Urville with the *Astrolabe* and *Zelée*, failed in the attempt to surpass the latitude of Weddell; they saw and renamed Joinville Island and Philippe Land. Various voyages were made by whalers, without important geographical results.

After his voyage in the African Quadrant (*q.v.*), Biscoe in the *Tula* made extensive discoveries west of Palmer Land, — Biscoe, Adelaide and other small islands; on February 15, 1832, he reached 67° 15′ S., 69° 29′ W.

Ross' third antarctic voyage was made in this quadrant, though without important results. He landed on Cockburn (Ross) Island, and then crossed the circle. On March 2, 1843, he made a sounding in 68° 14′ S., 12° 20′ W., from which he reported the depth to be 4,000 fathoms with no bottom; the depth is now known to be only 2,660 fathoms. For thirty years he had no successors but whalers.

Dallmann, in the German whaler *Gronland*, in 1873 mistook Bismarck Bay to be a strait. The

Scottish whalers *Active* and *Balaena* made no discoveries of value in 1892. The German sealer *Hertha*, under Evensen, passing Biscoe Islands and the mainland in 1893, reached, on November 21, 69° 10′ S., 76° 12′ W. Evensen sighted but did not reach Alexander Island. A German whaler, Larsen, the same year landed on Seymour Island and found the first sedimentary fossils. In 1894 he followed in the *Jason* the west coast of Palmer Land, which he named Oscar Land; skirting the coast continuously to 68° 10′ S., he saw two active volcanos and two nunataks, which he named Seal Islands.

The Belgian expedition of 1897–1899, under Gerlache in the *Belgica*, made extensive discoveries. It was notable for its efficient and experienced personnel, — Amundsen, Arctowski, Danco, Cook, Lecointe and Racovitza. A strait (Gerlache) was found to separate Graham Archipelago from the mainland. On March 5, 1898, the *Belgica* was beset, and for twelve months drifted to and fro. The drift was between 80° 30′ W. and 102° W., and carried her to 71° 32′ S., where she was over the continental shelf, the sea being only one hundred twenty fathoms deep. As the drift was to the south of Peter Island, its isolation was evident, as no other land was seen save Alexander Island.

The collections, made from eighteen different islands, were most valuable contributions to science. Arctowski collected mosses, lichens, grasses, musci, diptera, etc., hitherto unknown in antarctica : presumably they were importations through visiting birds. Basing his opinion partly on the continental plateau, and on the sea shallowing to the south, Racovitza considered it probable that there is "a continuing continental mass from longitude 50° W., to 60° E.", one of the supporting points being "the tereous nature of the sediments of the continental plateau containing a very strong proportion of sand, gravel and rounded pebbles."

Geographically, Gerlache corrected many erroneous longitudes of his predecessors, discovered Gerlache Strait and Danco Land, proving the existence of an extensive archipelago, to which he generously affixed the name of Palmer (Gerlache : "Quinze Mois dans l'Antarctique." 1902).

The Scottish expedition of 1902, under E. S. Bruce in the *Scotia*, attacked the Weddell Sea, where the ship was beset in 70° 25' S. The sea there was found to be 2,500 fathoms deep. After wintering in the South Orkneys, Bruce resumed his voyage in 1904. To the southward the soundings generally exceeded 2,600 fathoms to 72° S., 18° W., where the sea shallowed to 1,131 fathoms. On March 6, when the sea was only 159 fathoms deep, land was sighted. Ice floes prevented them from approaching nearer than within two miles, when they saw that it was an ice-covered, undulating region, which was named Coats Land. Their

Photograph by R. C. Murphy

Norwegian Whaling Station, Cumberland Bay, South Georgia.

farthest south was 74° 01′ S., 22° W., within fourteen miles of the southing of Weddell (Brown,
Mossman, Pirie: "Voyage of the *Scotia*." 1906).

Otto Nordenskiold, in the *Antarctic*, 1902,
wintered with five others on Seymour Island, their
ship returning. In exploring adjacent regions
Nordenskiold sledged four hundred miles to 66° S.,
where he found the island to be "an elevated
mountainous country, with rugged crests behind
which extends a large ice plateau, from which
immense glaciers descend." The Seal Islands
proved to be nunataks.

In 1905, Mt. Haddington proved to be on an
island. While exploring, he met two men of the
expected ship *Antarctic*, which had been wrecked.
Nordenskiold and the crew were finally rescued
by the Chilian frigate *Uruguay*, under Captain
Irizar.

The researches of Nordenskiold were varied and
important, covering magnetism, meteorology, biology and especially geology. He found strata
of the early Tertiary age, miscellaneous verte-
brates and leaf impressions indicating a former
luxuriant vegetation. Andersson of the expedition
found fossil flora on Philippe Land of the Jurassic
period, disclosing vegetation similar to the Upper
Gondwana of India (Nordenskiold and Andersson: "Antarctica." 1905).

In 1903–1904, Charcot in the *Français* wintered
at Wandel Island, at the south entrance to Gerlache

Strait. Explorations were made towards Alexander Island, which was surrounded by impassible ice. The western coasts of the Palmer Archipelago were charted and much valuable scientific data were collected. An unknown section of the continental coast was discovered, Loubet Land (Charcot: "Le Français au Pole Sud." 1906).

In 1908 Charcot resumed his explorations in the *Pourquoi pas*, during which he wintered at Petermann Island. He discovered certain new sections of the coast of Antarctica, which were named after Charcot and Fallier. He proved that Peter and Alexander are isolated islands, and made a remarkable exploration of the sea as far west as 124° W. (*Geographic Journal*).

In 1914 Shackleton initiated an expedition to cross the continent of Antarctica. The plan looked to the landing of Shackleton on Coats Land, whence he would cross to McMurdo Sound, where he would meet MacIntosh, who would be sent there in the *Aurora*. (For MacIntosh, see Chapter XXIII.)

Shackleton sailed from South Georgia in the *Endurance* on December 8, 1914. In Weddell Sea impenetrable ice fields prevented his landing on Coats Land. Continuing southward he discovered Caird Coast, an extension of Coats Land. Skirting the new coast for about two hundred miles, he found it to be a typical antarctic land, ice-covered and discharging immense glaciers,

which made landing impracticable. Prevented
by heavy ice from proceeding beyond 77° 40′
S., 35° W., he turned westward along the edge
of the heavy ice, in the direction of Palmer
Land. On February 15, 1915, the *Endurance* was
beset, and thereafter moved with the pack. She
was carried first to 77° S., 35° W., and eventually
to 69° 05′ S., 51° 32′ W., where she was crushed
and sank, after having drifted seven hundred
miles. By the most strenuous and skillful exertions
Shackleton landed the whole party on Elephant
Island, an ice-capped islet seven hundred fifty
miles from South Georgia, the nearest source of
relief. By a desperately hazardous voyage, with
superior seamanship he reached South Georgia,
and despite serious misadventures with the relief
ships, the entire party was rescued on August 30,
1916, by the Chilian ship *Yelcho* (Shackleton:
"South." 1892).

Weddell Sea was again entered by Filchner, in
1912, when he surpassed his predecessors by reaching in the *Deutschland* about 76° S., 40° W. He
extended Coats Land to the south, giving it the
name of Luitpold Land. Bare rocks were visible
about 25 miles inland.

Shackleton, in his final voyage, sailed in the
Quest from South Georgia, December 21, 1921, but
died at sea in March. His second in command,
Wild, continuing the expedition, was beset thirty-
five miles from "the appearance of land", reported

by Ross, but did not see it. He reported the non-existence of Pagoda Rock.

In 1908 the American Quadrant was transformed from an area of exploration into a field of commercial activity, whereby British interests were coördinated and consolidated. On July 21, Letters Patent under the Great Seal of Great Britain created the Dependencies of the Falkland Islands. They included the section from 20 degrees west longitude to 50 degrees west longitude, from the latitude 50° south to the South Pole. Also between longitudes 50° W., and 80° W., the section south of latitude 58° S. This covers a sector of the antarctic land area to the south and southwest of Cape Horn, and numerous islands in the Southern Ocean. The Letters Patent further vest a governor general, resident in the Falklands, with the administration of the Falkland Islands, of South Georgia, of South Orkney Islands, of the South Shetland Islands, of the South Sandwich Islands and of Graham Land.

The effect of this organization is the control of more than a million square miles of seas, easily accessible for fishing, sealing and whaling, which is now permitted only under licenses granted by the Governor General. The protests of Spain and Argentina against the declaration of British sovereignty have been unavailing. The seas are now exploited by Norwegian whalers, fishing under British licenses.

INDEX

INDEX

Index

Index